PR⊙MS

GW00643631

The BBC presents the 111th season
of Henry Wood Promenade Concerts

PROMS
15 JULY – 10 SEPTEMBER 2005

THE PROMS: 1895–2005

The Proms were founded to bring the best of classical music to a wide audience in an informal setting. From the very outset, part of the audience has always stood in the 'promenade' [a]. Prom places originally cost just a shilling; today, standing places at the Royal Albert Hall still cost only £4.00, and over 1,000 tickets go on sale for every concert from an hour beforehand. Programmes have always mixed the great classics with what Henry Wood, the first conductor of the Proms, called his 'novelties' – in other words, rare works and premieres.

1895 The 26-year-old Henry Wood [b] is chosen to launch the Promenade Concerts at the newly opened Queen's Hall, Langham Place [c]; Wood conducts the Proms throughout their first 50 years. **1905** Wood composes his celebrated *Fantasia on·British Sea-Songs* for a special Trafalgar Day concert. **1927** The BBC takes over the running of the Proms. **1930** The new BBC Symphony Orchestra becomes the orchestra of the Proms; the BBC's own orchestras still provide the backbone of the season. **1941** The Proms move to the Royal Albert Hall after the Queen's Hall is gutted in an air raid. **1942** The BBC SO shares the season for the first time with another orchestra: the LPO. **1944** Wood dies shortly after celebrating his Proms jubilee. **1947** First televised Last Night. **1953** First out-of-London orchestra at the Proms: the Hallé, from Manchester, under John Barbirolli. **1960** First BBC Proms commission: William Alwyn's *Derby Day*. **1961** First complete opera at the Proms: Mozart's *Don Giovanni*, brought by Glyndebourne Festival. **1966** First foreign orchestra at the Proms: the Moscow Radio Orchestra, under Gennady Rozhdestvensky. **1968** First Friday-night First Night. **1970** First Late Night Prom: cult pop group The Soft Machine. **1971** First 'world music' Prom: sitar-player Imrat Khan. **1974** First Pre-Prom Talks. **1994** The Proms celebrate their 100th season with a retrospective of past premieres. **1995** The Proms celebrate their centenary year with a season of new commissions. **1996** First Proms Chamber Music series; first Prom in the Park [d]. **1998** First Blue Peter Family Prom [e]. **2002** The Proms go digital on BBC4. **2003** Proms in the Park reach out to include all four nations of the UK in the unique festive atmosphere of the Last Night [f]. **2005** Proms Chamber Music moves to Cadogan Hall, the movies return to the Proms, and Henry Wood's *Sea-Song Fantasia* celebrates its centenary.

The BBC: bringing the Proms to you – in concert, on radio, television and online bbc.co.uk/proms

WELCOME TO THE BBC PROMS 2005!

For 110 years the Proms have brought great music-making to London every summer, and since the BBC took over the Proms in 1927, millions around the world have been able to enjoy the concerts – first on radio, then on television and now online.

This season we welcome the Royal Concertgebouw Orchestra with its new music director Mariss Jansons, the Vienna Philharmonic with Christoph Eschenbach and Zubin Mehta, the Cleveland Orchestra under Franz Welser-Möst and the World Orchestra for Peace with Valery Gergiev, while The Royal Opera under Antonio Pappano continues our Proms *Ring* cycle with *Die Walküre*, in which Plácido Domingo makes his long-awaited Proms debut.

THE SEA To celebrate the Year of the Sea, 200 years after Trafalgar, Sir John Eliot Gardiner conducts Haydn's 'Nelson' Mass, Sir Charles Mackerras conducts Gilbert & Sullivan's *HMS Pinafore*, Esa-Pekka Salonen marks the centenary of Debussy's *La mer*, and other seascapes flow throughout the season, from Vaughan Williams's *A Sea Symphony* to Britten's 'Four Sea Interludes' from *Peter Grimes*.

FAIRY TALES Born 200 years ago, Hans Christian Andersen has inspired composers from Stravinsky and Zemlinsky to Bent Sørensen, who has written a new work on *The Little Mermaid*. Purcell's *The Fairy Queen* and Mendelssohn's *A Midsummer Night's Dream* lead the season's fairy dance.

ANNIVERSARIES Michael Tippett, one of the most inspirational composers of our time, would have been 100 this year; among several other major works, his *A Child of Our Time* marks the anniversary of the end of World War II, which also brings Górecki's Third Symphony to the Proms. Other anniversaries – from Tallis and Carissimi to Rawsthorne and Lambert, Berg and Berio – are also celebrated.

The Proms continue to expand: our successful lunchtime chamber music concerts move to the fine new Cadogan Hall near Sloane Square. We bring talented young musicians to perform alongside the BBC Symphony Orchestra in a day dedicated to the violin. Many new works are heard from the leading BBC and UK orchestras, and we welcome the legendary Ravi Shankar, Baaba Maal and Bobby McFerrin.

Join us for a superlative summer of music-making, and enjoy the season!

Nicholas Kenyon

Nicholas Kenyon Director, BBC Proms

THE SEA

FROM OUT THE AZURE MAIN

Two hundred years after Nelson's 'great and glorious victory' over the French
fleet at Trafalgar, and a century after Debussy made the finishing touches to
La mer while holidaying on this side of the English Channel, **Anthony Burton**
examines why composers through the ages have been so keen to put to sea

ABOVE
Horatio, Lord Nelson:
1801 portrait
by Sir William Beechey

ABOVE RIGHT
'England expects that
every man will do his duty':
The Death of Nelson
(1859–64) by Daniel Maclise

RIGHT
*The Battle of Trafalgar,
21 October 1805*: 1816
coloured print after a painting
by Thomas Whitcombe

More than nine-tenths of the earth's surface is occupied by sea. Many millions of us live near the sea, and use it for work or recreation. But, as recent events have starkly reminded us, it can be a terrible force for destruction as well as an indispensable resource for humanity. For centuries it has provided most of the world's long-distance trade routes, and it has been the scene of many of its decisive battles.

Notable among these is the Battle of Trafalgar, on 21 October 1805, a crucial event in the history of our own island nation, in which Admiral Nelson defeated Napoleon's fleet but lost his life in the process. The bicentenary of this event is the occasion for a year-long national festival, *SeaBritain 2005*. It's also commemorated in this Proms season by the Haydn Mass that has become associated with Nelson's name, as well as by the traditional Last Night performance of Sir Henry Wood's *Fantasia on British Sea-Songs*, composed in 1905 for the Trafalgar centenary and so celebrating its own centenary this year.

But, beyond this, the Proms explore some of the vast range of music associated with the sea – and the possibilities are as endless as the oceans. The sea has provided innumerable settings, images and metaphors for librettists and composers. In the earliest known song-cycle, the 13th-century *Cantigas*

Henry Wood (1869–1944) *Fantasia on British Sea-Songs*

Henry Wood, the founder-conductor of the Proms, compiled his *Fantasia on British Sea-Songs* for a special matinée Prom on 21 October 1905 (the season ran later in the year in those days) celebrating the centenary of the Battle of Trafalgar. Within a few years, to his surprise, it had become a staple item on the menu of the Last Night. And there it remains to this day, albeit considerably modified over the years, most recently as the agent to bind together the four nations of the United Kingdom in Proms in the Park concerts across the country. This year, to mark the centenary of the piece and the bicentenary of the occasion it celebrates, the *Fantasia* will have restored to it Wood's introductory sequence of authentic naval bugle-calls. These will usher in his pot-pourri of sea-songs (and a hornpipe), augmented by national songs from around the British Isles, but ending as usual with Wood's own versions of Handel's 'See the conqu'ring hero comes' (not that Nelson lived to receive such a welcome) and Thomas Arne's 'Rule, Britannia!'.

de amigo by Martin Codax, the singer takes the part of a girl waiting for her sailor lover to return to the port of Vigo. Shakespeare's *The Tempest* includes the haunting sea dirge 'Full fathom five', memorably set by several composers, including Michael Tippett (whose centenary we celebrate this year) in his incidental music for a 1961 production of the play – music that was later added to at the end of his life and expanded into a large-scale *Tempest* suite in response to a 1995 BBC commission for the *Fairest Isle* season.

The lovely lute-song 'Never weather-beaten sail', with words and music by Shakespeare's near-contemporary Thomas Campion, compares a ship heading for shore with the soul longing for rest. And many arias in Baroque opera rely on marine imagery: for example 'Da tempesta il legno

infranto' in Handel's *Julius Caesar*, this year's Glyndebourne offering (*see 'Season Highlights', page 72*), in which Cleopatra celebrates finding happiness with Caesar, as a 'boat crushed by the storm' still reaches port safely.

Composers who lived close to the sea perhaps had an unfair advantage. Vivaldi, a native of Venice who taught at the Pietà convent right on the waterfront, composed several concertos with the title *La tempesta di mare* ('The storm at sea'), as well as one called *La concha*, after the conch trumpet of the sea-god Triton. Telemann, who spent many years in the northern port city of Hamburg, wrote a suite called *Hamburger Ebb' und Flut* ('Hamburg Ebb and Flow'), including dances named after Triton and his fellow gods, goddesses and sea-nymphs,

FAR LEFT
'If by your art, my dearest father, you have put the wild waters in this roar, allay them': *Miranda* (1916) by John William Waterhouse

LEFT
Sea-view of the Free and Hanseatic City of Hamburg: engraving by Peter van der Doort (*fl.*1590–1602)

BELOW
Going with the flow: Hamburg's 18th-century director of music, Georg Philipp Telemann

Georg Philipp Telemann (1681–1767)
Suite 'Hamburger Ebb' und Flut'

PROM 29

Georg Philipp Telemann, friend of Handel and Bach and godfather to Bach's son Carl Philipp Emanuel, was director of music in the bustling North German port city of Hamburg from 1721 until his death in 1767, and wrote music for many civic occasions. Among them, in 1723, was the centenary of the city's College of Admiralty, which regulated many aspects of maritime life. For the celebratory banquet, Telemann wrote both a vocal serenata and a characteristically colourful and tuneful orchestral suite, *Hamburg Ebb and Flow*. The latter is sometimes called *Wassermusik*, which makes it sound like a counterpart to Handel's *Water Music*. But whereas the Handel was written for one or more royal river trips, the Telemann is definitely sea music. An overture of alternating calm and storm, full of suggestions of wave movement, is followed by a sequence of dances with titles referring to the sea deities Thetis, Neptune and Triton, the Naiads at play, and the wind gods 'tempestuous Aeolus' and 'pleasant Zephyr'. Then the music comes ashore with lively dances called 'Hamburg Ebb and Flow' (a reference to the tides that daily flushed out the city's sewers) and 'The merry sailors'.

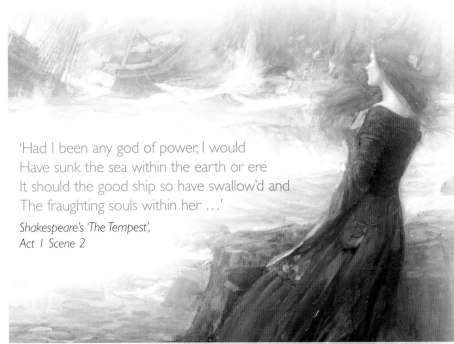

'Had I been any god of power, I would
Have sunk the sea within the earth or ere
It should the good ship so have swallow'd and
The fraughting souls within her ...'

*Shakespeare's 'The Tempest',
Act 1 Scene 2*

Joseph Haydn (1732–1809) *Missa in angustiis ('Nelson' Mass)*

Haydn's *Missa in angustiis* ('Mass in time of peril') – the most urgent and austere of his masterly late series of settings of the Latin Mass for the Esterházy family – was written in the summer of 1798. This was a time when the Allies' war against Revolutionary France was going badly, and much of Austria was occupied by the French. According to one account (on which recent scholarship has cast doubt), the war also impinged on the Mass in a more specific way. Haydn, it is said, was at work on it when a courier arrived with the news of Nelson's victory over the French at Aboukir, and the announcement became translated into musical terms as the stirring trumpet fanfare at the end of the 'Benedictus'. However, the nickname of 'Nelson' Mass stems not from this moment, but from a visit which Nelson, together with Sir William and Lady Hamilton, paid to the Esterházy palace at Eisenstadt in September 1800 – a visit which is said (though the scholars have questioned this as well) to have included a performance of Haydn's Mass.

but ending with a cheerful number for the 'merry sailors'. (Purcell would no doubt have approved: in the midst of the tragic love-story of his *Dido and Aeneas*, a sailor enjoins his colleagues to take 'a boozy short leave of your nymphs on the shore'.)

In the Classical era, some leading composers never strayed far from the land-locked heart of Europe. Beethoven never saw the sea; nor, despite his portrayals of whirlpool and lagoon, did Schubert. But Mozart crossed the English Channel at the age of 8, not without what his father Leopold called 'a heavy contribution in vomiting', and returned a year and a half later with fair weather and a following wind. Memories of the first voyage may well have contributed to the exceptionally graphic storm music in his sea-girt opera *Idomeneo*; and of the second perhaps to 'Soave sia il vento', the send-off given the two young men in *Così fan tutte* on their (feigned) departure across the Bay of Naples.

Mozart's friend Haydn made his first Channel crossing at the more advanced age of 58, suffering first of all a calm that restricted the ship to a mile's progress in

four hours, then a gale. 'So long as it was calm, I wasn't afraid at all,' he wrote to a friend, 'but towards the end, when the wind grew stronger and stronger, and I saw the monstrous high waves rushing at us, I became a little frightened, and a little indisposed, too.' Shortly thereafter he composed his 'madrigal' *The Storm*.

Haydn's experience is a reminder that in Goethe's pair of poems 'Calm Sea' and 'Prosperous Voyage', set as a choral cantata by Beethoven and made the subject of an overture by Mendelssohn, the two titles are opposites and not complementary: in the age of sail, a calm sea got you nowhere. However, by the time Elgar

Bridgeman Art Library (above); Lebrecht Music & Arts (right)

ABOVE
A patriotic tribute to Nelson: anonymous painted panel, c1820

RIGHT
'When the wind grew stronger and stronger, and I saw the monstrous high waves rushing at us, I became a little frightened, and a little indisposed, too': *Haydn's Stormy Channel Crossing* by Sammon

Felix Mendelssohn (1809–47)
Overture 'The Hebrides' ('Fingal's Cave')

PROM 11

In August 1829, during a tour of Scotland, Mendelssohn and his friend Klingemann visited Fingal's Cave on the Hebridean island of Staffa: a magnet for tourists not only because of its dramatic scenery, but also because it was the reputed home of the ancient bard Ossian, the 'translations' of whose poetry had become celebrated all over Europe. On the spot, as a letter to his father including 21 scribbled bars of music confirms, Mendelssohn conceived the opening of the great orchestral seascape which at one time he planned to call *The Lonely Isle*, but which is now known as *The Hebrides* or *Fingal's Cave* overture. However, he went on working on the piece over the next three years, struggling to reconcile the demands of descriptive tone-painting and Classical form – a struggle summed up in his wry lament, in a letter of January 1832, that 'the whole so-called development smells more of counterpoint than of blubber, gulls and salted cod'.

quoted Mendelssohn's overture in the last but one of his *Enigma Variations*, wishing a retrospective 'bon voyage' to whichever friend is concealed beneath the code-name ***, the age of steam had taken over, and the quotation is accompanied by a quiet timpani roll suggesting a ship's engines.

In the 19th century, many composers wrote about the sea from personal experience. Mendelssohn conceived the opening of his concert overture *The Hebrides* (or *Fingal's Cave*) while actually at sea *en route* to the island of Staffa. Berlioz's overture *The Corsair*, named after Byron's poem about a Mediterranean pirate, was

first drafted when he was staying by the Mediterranean at Nice. A storm-tossed journey in the Baltic and the North Sea inspired the tempestuous music of Wagner's operatic overture *The Flying Dutchman*. Richest of all in first-hand experience was Rimsky-Korsakov, who spent two and a half years travelling the world as an officer on a Russian merchant ship and whose orchestral suite *Sheherazade* contains as many scenes of sea and shipwreck as of fairy-tale enchantment.

In Victorian and Edwardian Britain, made safe largely by the dominance of the Royal Navy and made rich largely by the activities of the merchant fleet, the glorious naval past was a favourite topic. One specialist in it was Stanford, whose popularity stemmed chiefly from his choral cantatas *The Revenge* and *The Battle of the Baltic*, the *Songs of the Sea* and the later *Songs of the Fleet*. These works seem to have been admired above all for their masculine virtues: one commentator, as late as 1921,

Richard Wagner (1813–83) *The Flying Dutchman – overture*

PROM 59

Wagner's 'romantic opera' *The Flying Dutchman*, first performed in Dresden in 1843 and one of the most popular of his early works, is based on a legend of the sea, as retold by Heinrich Heine. Its central figure is a Dutch sea-captain who is punished for blasphemy by being condemned to sail the seas for ever, until he is redeemed by a woman's love. The overture is a tone-poem dominated by the musical depiction of a storm-tossed sea – something Wagner himself had experienced on a difficult crossing from the Baltic coast to London in 1839. He later recalled the moment when his ship had sought shelter in a Norwegian fjord: 'An inexpressible happiness seized hold of me when the echo of the immense granite walls threw back the shout of the crew … The short rhythmic cries settled in me like a mightily comforting portent and soon formed into the theme of the sailors' song in my *Flying Dutchman*, the idea of which I already carried within me.'

TOP
It is, it is a glorious thing: a piratical portrait of Lord Byron in Albanian dress (1813), by Thomas Phillips

ABOVE
Felix Mendelssohn: watercolour by James Warren Childe, painted in 1829, the year of the composer's visit to Fingal's Cave

FAR LEFT
Staffa, Fingal's Cave (1832) by J. M. W. Turner

LEFT
Lover's leap: Senta dives to her death to save the Dutchman from eternal damnation in the final scene of Wagner's sea-swept opera, as staged at its 1843 Dresden premiere

went out of his way to praise Stanford for arranging the choral part of the *Songs of the Fleet* for male voices only, 'thus removing the last trace that there may have been of any womanish influence on the work'. (What would the author have thought of Ellen MacArthur's record-breaking solo circumnavigation under sail?) Such nautical manliness was duly sent up by Gilbert and Sullivan in their 1878 operetta *HMS Pinafore* (see 'Season Highlights', page 67), to which *Pineapple Poll* – the 1951 ballet score arranged by Charles Mackerras from Sullivan's music, and also set in Portsmouth Harbour (where Nelson's flagship *Victory* is still docked) – provides a saucily feminine foil.

FAR RIGHT
Walking the plank: Elaine Fifield as Pineapple Poll in the 1951 Sadler's Wells premiere of John Cranko and Charles Mackerras's Sullivan-based ballet

INSET RIGHT
Drumming them up the Channel: 1581 portrait of Sir Francis Drake by Nicholas Hilliard

BELOW
Charles Villiers Stanford: portrait photograph, c1905

BOTTOM
Plunket Greene: the Irish bass-baritone for whom Stanford composed his *Songs of the Sea*

Charles Villiers Stanford (1852–1924)
Songs of the Sea

Charles Villiers Stanford was born in Dublin, but became a pillar of musical life in London and Cambridge, teaching two generations of British composers, including Vaughan Williams, Holst, Bridge, Bliss and Howells. His *Songs of the Sea* are settings of five poems by Sir Henry Newbolt that link the glories of the British naval past to the tense international situation of his own time. Typical is the first song, 'Drake's Drum', in which Sir Francis Drake, asleep for centuries, promises:

If the Dons sight Devon, I'll quit the port of Heaven,
And drum them up the Channel as we drummed them long ago.

The songs, composed for the baritone Plunket Greene and first performed as a set in 1904, can be sung by any combination from voice and piano to solo baritone, male chorus and orchestra, and their memorable melodies soon made them popular in the drawing-room as well as the concert hall. Three of them were included in the first ever BBC broadcast of a Henry Wood Promenade Concert in August 1927.

PROM
35

PORTSMOUTH POINT

The mood of nautical retrospection persisted well into the 20th century. Walton's 1925 *Portsmouth Point* overture, his earliest orchestral work to reach performance, was inspired by an etching of a busy quayside scene by the 18th-century artist Thomas Rowlandson; and, for all its up-to-date, jazzy rhythms, it suggests a much more traditional vein of roistering – as if, Michael Kennedy memorably suggests, 'the sailors of HMS *Pinafore* had had a night on the tiles'. In 1940, Erich Wolfgang Korngold provided a suitably swashbuckling score for *The Sea Hawk*, starring Errol Flynn as an Elizabethan privateer at large on the Spanish Main. But in the same year, Walton's friend Constant Lambert (born 100 years ago this August) was painting an altogether more contemporary picture of 'the heroism and gaiety of the Merchant Navy' in his score for the wartime documentary film *Merchant Seamen*.

The sea offered a rich seam of metaphor and allegory to English and American writers in the 19th century, meeting a correspondingly rich (though sometimes delayed) reaction from composers. Matthew Arnold's profound nocturnal meditation *Dover Beach* was set by Samuel Barber in 1931. Herman Melville's encyclopaedic novel *Moby Dick* found no musical equivalent until Bernard Herrmann's cantata of 1938, while his novella *Billy Budd*, set on board ship in the Napoleonic Wars, was turned into an opera by Britten only in 1951. Walt Whitman's sea poems, in which the ocean is the setting for elemental scenes of love, loss and voyaging towards death, were seized on rather more quickly by British composers – in particular by Vaughan Williams in his hugely ambitious *A Sea Symphony* of 1910.

TOP LEFT
Jolly Jack Tars take a boozy short leave of their nymphs on the shore: *Portsmouth Point* by Thomas Rowlandson (1756–1827)

BOTTOM LEFT
Matthew Arnold, poet of *Dover Beach*

BELOW
Errol Flynn buckles his swash and swishes his sword as an Elizabethan privateer in *The Sea Hawk*

Samuel Barber (1910–81) *Dover Beach*

Matthew Arnold's great poem *Dover Beach* is a meditation by the English Channel at night. The sea becomes a factor unifying past and present: just as the poet hears in the sound of wave-borne pebbles 'the eternal note of sadness', so Sophocles once heard 'the turbid ebb and flow of human misery'. It also provides a metaphor for the loss of Victorian certainties:

The Sea of Faith
Was once, too, at the full, and round earth's shore
Lay like the folds of a bright girdle furl'd.
But now I only hear
Its melancholy, long, withdrawing roar …

In 1931, while he was still a student at the Curtis Institute in Philadelphia, Samuel Barber set the poem for baritone and string quartet, using the strings to suggest the ever-present background of the sea. Soon after completing the work, he sang it, accompanying himself on the piano, to Vaughan Williams. He was delighted by the older composer's comment: 'I myself once set *Dover Beach*, but you really got it!'

Two years later came Frank Bridge's 1912 suite *The Sea*, a later performance of which left the 10-year-old Benjamin Britten 'knocked sideways' and encouraged him to seek lessons from the older composer. The influence of Bridge's *The Sea* can be traced in some passages, and two of the titles, of the 'Four Sea Interludes' in Britten's own opera, *Peter Grimes*.

ABOVE
'O my brave Soul, O farther, farther sail!': Walt Whitman, the American poet whose verses Vaughan Williams set in his *Sea Symphony*

RIGHT
'I am native, rooted here': Benjamin Britten on the beach at Aldeburgh, the Suffolk fishing village where his opera *Peter Grimes* is set and where the composer later made his home

Benjamin Britten (1913–76)

PROM **68**

Peter Grimes – 'Four Sea Interludes'

The sea is almost a character in *Peter Grimes*, the work which in 1945 launched Benjamin Britten on his career as one of the most successful opera composers of modern times. Based on an episode in George Crabbe's 1810 poem *The Borough* (set in Aldeburgh, the Suffolk coastal town where Britten went to live), the opera depicts an intolerant, gossip-ridden community uniting against the fisherman Peter Grimes, a recluse who is really at home only on the sea. Of the four 'Sea Interludes' which Britten extracted from the score to form a concert suite, two are straightforward portrayals of nature: the opening picture of a grey North Sea 'Dawn', and the third interlude, 'Moonlight'. 'Sunday Morning' combines a depiction of the 'glitter of waves and glitter of sunlight' with the sound of church bells on shore as the townsfolk go to their pious prayers. And in the final interlude, the turmoil of a 'Storm' raging over sea and land reflects the turmoil raging in Peter Grimes's mind, sweeping away a moment of calm: 'What harbour shelters peace, away from tidal waves, away from storms?'

Ralph Vaughan Williams (1872–1958) *A Sea Symphony*

PROM **11**

One of the great classics of sea music, from its thrilling opening to its infinitely remote epilogue, is Vaughan Williams's First Symphony. This was one of the earliest symphonies to employ voices throughout – alongside Mahler's Eighth, also first performed in 1910. The work's ambitious nature matches that of the texts, by the American poet Walt Whitman. The opening 'Song for All Seas, All Ships' celebrates not only the sea itself but also the intrepid sailors of all countries, and commemorates those lost at sea. 'On the Beach at Night Alone' is a meditation on the 'vast similitude' embracing 'all nations, all identities, ... all lives and deaths'. 'The Waves' is a brilliant scherzo. The finale, 'The Explorers', treats a sea voyage as a metaphor for the soul's journey towards death and transcendence:

O we can wait no longer, We too take ship, O Soul, Joyous we too launch out on trackless seas, Fearless for unknown shores on waves of ecstasy to sail ...

'In writing *Peter Grimes* I wanted to express my awareness of the perpetual struggle of men and women whose livelihood depends on the sea.'
Benjamin Britten, 1945

LA MER

Claude Debussy (1862–1918)
La mer

PROM 73

'You perhaps do not know that I was destined for the fine life of a sailor and that it was only by chance that I was led away from it. But I still have a great passion for the sea.' So Debussy wrote to a colleague in September 1903 as he was beginning work on *La mer* ('The Sea'), perhaps his most perfectly finished work for orchestra. He composed it over the next 18 months, mostly far inland in Burgundy, but also during holidays on the Normandy coast and in the Channel Islands; and he reputedly corrected the proofs of the score while staying at the Sussex seaside resort of Eastbourne. As movement titles such as 'Play of the waves' and 'Dialogue of the wind and the sea' suggest, the work is full of detailed nature-painting. At the same time, its subtitle of 'three symphonic sketches' implies that the music has its own structure and should not be taken too literally. Debussy's friend Erik Satie made this point with characteristic wit when he said about the first movement, 'From dawn to midday on the sea', that he liked it all 'but especially the bit at a quarter to eleven'.

Perhaps the greatest of all early 20th-century musical seascapes was Debussy's *La mer*, completed and first performed 100 years ago this year. In this masterpiece, the influence of the sea was mediated not through literature but through the visual arts: Debussy may well have been inspired to start it by seeing some sea paintings by Turner, whom he considered 'the greatest creator of mysterious effects in the whole world of art'; and he asked for Hokusai's print *The Hollow of the Wave off Kanagawa* to be reproduced on the cover of the score.

Much more recently, Turner paintings, again largely seascapes, have also been the inspiration for Thea Musgrave's *Turbulent Landscapes* – one more example of the huge influence the sea continues to exercise on composers, as on artists, writers and all of mankind.

BELOW
Looking out to sea:
Thea Musgrave

RIGHT
Sunrise with Sea Monsters (c1845): one of the Turner seascapes that inspired Musgrave's new work

Musgrave: Sunrise with Sea Monsters (below), Tate Picture Library (right)

Thea Musgrave (born 1928)

Turbulent Landscapes (London premiere)

PROM 6

Thea Musgrave, Scottish-born but a resident of the USA since 1970, is an experienced composer of operas, and her concert works have frequently been inspired by dramatic scenarios, or by extra-musical stimuli from literature, history and the visual arts. *Turbulent Landscapes*, her most recent orchestral work, was written in 2003 in response to a commission from the Boston Symphony Orchestra, and was given its UK premiere by the BBC Symphony Orchestra on a visit to Manchester last November. Its six movements were suggested by paintings by J. M. W. Turner, including several of his many seascapes, both topographic and visionary: the first movement by *Sunrise with Sea Monsters*; the second by three works, *Staffa, Fingal's Cave* (which prompts a fleeting reference back to Mendelssohn), *The Shipwreck* and *The Dawn after the Wreck*; the last by *Sunrise, with a Boat between Headlands*. The composer says that 'the turbulence of the title represents some kind of "event" that is wonderfully depicted in the various paintings of Turner. ... To heighten the drama, in each of the movements the protagonist is characterised by a solo player from the orchestra.'

For more 'New Music' at the Proms 2005, see pages 50–57

'Sea' music at the Proms 2005

Barber	Dover Beach	PCM 1
Berlioz	The Corsair	Prom 1
Britten	Peter Grimes – 'Four Sea Interludes'	Prom 68
Carissimi	Jonah	PCM 7
Debussy	La mer	Prom 73
Fauré	L'Horizon chimérique	PCM 1
Haydn	Missa in angustiis ('Nelson' Mass)	Prom 7
Korngold	The Sea Hawk – suite	Prom 74
Lambert	Merchant Seamen – suite	Prom 35
Mendelssohn	Overture 'The Hebrides' ('Fingal's Cave')	Prom 11
Musgrave	Turbulent Landscapes	Prom 6
Rimsky-Korsakov	Sheherazade	Prom 57
Stanford	Songs of the Sea	Prom 35
Sullivan	HMS Pinafore; Pineapple Poll	Prom 2
Telemann	Suite 'Hamburger Ebb' und Flut'	Prom 29
Tippett	The Tempest – suite	Prom 70
Vaughan Williams	A Sea Symphony	Prom 11
Wagner	The Flying Dutchman – overture	Prom 59
Walton	Overture 'Portsmouth Point'	Prom 74
Wood	Fantasia on British Sea-Songs	Prom 74

symphony hall
birmingham

'Symphony Hall never fails to surprise the ears and delight the spirits'
The Times, February 2001

'an inspiration to the orchestra... an inspiration also to its audiences' The Times

Photo: Adrian Burrows

'The best concert hall in the country'
Daily Telegraph

box office 0121 780 3333

online box office www.symphonyhall.co.uk/boxoffice
www.symphonyhall.co.uk admin tel: +44 (0)121 200 2000
fax: +44 (0)121 212 1982 email: symphonyhall@necgroup.co.uk

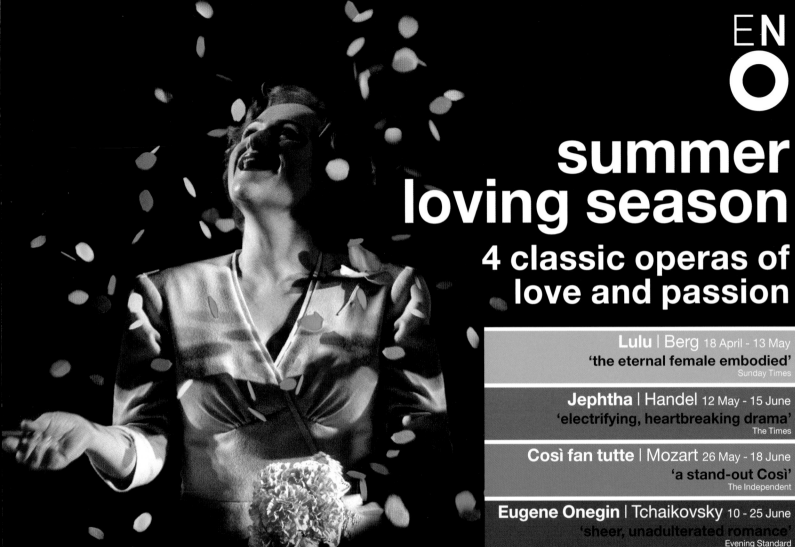

ENO

summer loving season

4 classic operas of love and passion

Lulu | Berg 18 April - 13 May
'the eternal female embodied'
Sunday Times

Jephtha | Handel 12 May - 15 June
'electrifying, heartbreaking drama'
The Times

Così fan tutte | Mozart 26 May - 18 June
'a stand-out Così'
The Independent

Eugene Onegin | Tchaikovsky 10 - 25 June
'sheer, unadulterated romance'
Evening Standard

ENO live at the London Coliseum
From £8. Buy online **www.eno.org** or call **020 7632 8300**

Photography : Laurie Lewis
Registered Charity no. 257210

eXQuisite

series

www.kef.com

If you're into sound, there's huge pleasure to be had from wideband formats like SACD and DVD-A. But to get the full benefit, you need a bit more than the same old speaker technology in a square wooden box.

That's where the new XQ Series comes in. Sure, they look the part – but what makes them so special is how they perform. The illusion of presence they create is so real it's scary. The detailing is phenomenal,

wherever you sit - even at super audio frequencies. We're talking total immersion in a way that's simply not possible with conventional systems.

No wonder – the XQ is packed with high end technologies from the latest Reference Series, including KEF's radical new Hypertweeter™ and the most sophisticated UNI-Q® arrays ever made. Hardware that changes your pulse rate. Please yourself.

KKEF®

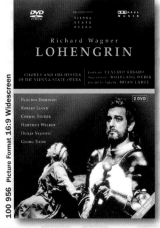
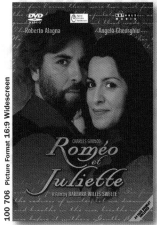

the voice of classical music

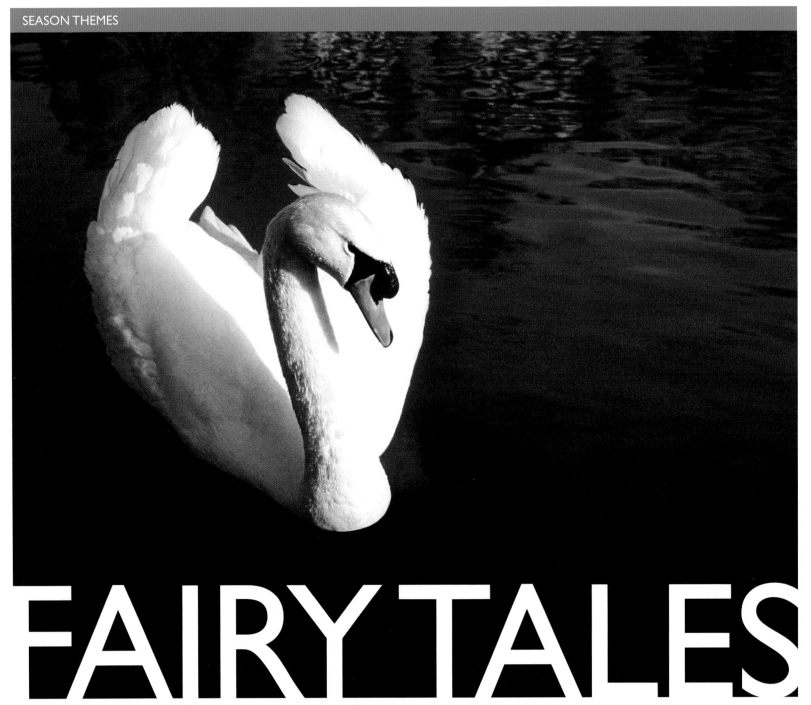

FAIRYTALES

IN THE LAND OF MAKE-BELIEVE

As the world celebrates Hans Christian Andersen's bicentenary, **Nicholas Tucker** argues that you don't have to believe in fairies to believe in the enduring power of fairy tales, while **Louise Downes** previews key fantasy pieces in this year's Proms

Collection of the New-York Historical Society (right)

Hans Christian Andersen's childhood reads as strangely as some of his own fairy tales. At home, he had a mad grandfather who used to sing in the streets, garlanded with flowers, and an aunt who worked in a brothel. The only son of a shoemaker and an illiterate washerwoman, as a child he played with the future King Frederik VII of Denmark at Odense Castle, where his mother worked. Rumours that the boys were half-brothers, with Hans the farmed-out illegitimate offspring of the Danish Crown Prince, persist to this day. Tall, awkward and effeminate, this classic 'ugly duckling' was also a compulsive exhibitionist, eager to recite, sing or dance whether his audience wanted him to or, more often, did not.

At 20 years old, in 1825, he was a horrified spectator at a public beheading. Immediately after the event a half-paralysed

TOP RIGHT
Hans Christian Andersen: ugly duckling or nightingale?

RIGHT
Black-paper silhouette of Andersen with the 'Swedish nightingale', Jenny Lind

Igor Stravinsky (1882–1971) *The Nightingale*

Hans Christian Andersen's *The Nightingale* enshrines a recurring motif in his work – the triumph of truth and natural talent over falsehood and mere imitation. Unlike the mechanical rival against whom she declines to compete, the little nightingale cannot be made to sing at anyone's command, not even an emperor's, yet her song, when truly valued and freely given, can (like that of an avian Orpheus) charm even Death itself.

The story's Chinese setting was inspired by the pagodas, peacocks and coloured lanterns of Copenhagen's newly-opened Tivoli Gardens, but its psychological origins lay closer to home: as an adolescent, Andersen may have been an ugly duckling, but his fine singing voice had earned him the nickname 'The Little Nightingale'; 25 years later, when he wrote the tale, his voice may have broken, but so had his heart, following a madly unrequited passion for Jenny Lind, the Scandinavian singing sensation popularly known as 'The Swedish Nightingale'.

Stravinsky's operatic setting of Andersen's tale should have been his first stage work, but barely had he completed the first of its three acts, in the summer of 1909, when a telegram arrived from Diaghilev urgently commissioning him to compose *The Firebird*, and the rest, as they say, is ballet history. It was

only four years later, after completing not only *The Firebird* but also *Petrushka* and *The Rite of Spring*, that Stravinsky was free to resume work on *The Nightingale*, by which time he had irreversibly outgrown his early late-Romantic style. Yet, ever the pragmatist, he brilliantly disguised the discrepancy by playing up the inherent contrast between the opening night-time forest scene, with its dappled echoes of Debussy and haunting Fisherman's Song, and the last two scenes set at the Imperial Court, whose spectacular compendium of exotically fantastical *chinoiserie* and pentatonic pomp, interspersed with the astral coloratura of the real songbird and grotesque warblings of her clockwork rival, climaxes in an eerily orchestrated duel between Death and the Nightingale at the foot of the Emperor's bed.

Igor Stravinsky (1882–1971)

PROM 15

The Fairy's Kiss

Stravinsky revered Tchaikovsky above all other composers. So when Ida Rubinstein asked him to create a new ballet for 1928, the 35th anniversary of his idol's death, he couldn't resist, even though he must have known this 'act of disloyalty' would end his friendship with Diaghilev, the great impresario who had nurtured his career for the past 20 years. Significantly, perhaps, his search for a suitable scenario took him back to the tales of that 'great poet with a gentle, sensitive soul' whose *Nightingale* he had been in the process of setting when Diaghilev first entered his life.

Now, re-reading Andersen's work, he came across a story he had forgotten 'which struck me as being the very thing for the idea that I wanted to express'. Typical of the Dane's later, more fatalistic style, *The Ice Maiden*, written in Switzerland in 1861, is the story of Rudy, a young Alpine mountaineer who, on the eve of his wedding to a wealthy miller's daughter, is finally reclaimed by the spirit of the great glacier from whose freezing embrace he had been saved as a baby many years before. To Stravinsky, the story suggested 'an allegory of Tchaikovsky himself. The fairy's kiss on the heel of the child is also the muse marking Tchaikovsky at his birth.' But the allegory was perhaps more accurate than Stravinsky knew, or was willing to say. For Andersen, who began an affair with a male dancer shortly after writing the story, the prospect of Rudy marrying anyone was clearly a fate worse than death and the icy kiss of the *femme fatale* a blessed release; while Tchaikovsky, who shared Andersen's ambivalent sexuality and had been driven nearly mad by a rash marriage to a woman

he barely knew, may well have killed himself to avoid a homosexual scandal.

But Stravinsky's 'heartfelt homage to Tchaikovsky's wonderful talent' is perhaps too innocent to bear that weight of interpretation. Knowing the story's Alpine setting from his own six-year stay in Switzerland during and after World War I, he said he pictured the rustic scenes 'with some of the performers dressed in the manner of early tourists and mingling with the friendly villagers in the good old theatrical tradition'. Part patchwork, part pastiche, the score weaves Stravinsky's orchestrations of lesser-known Tchaikovsky songs and piano pieces so closely with new music of his own devising, written in imitation of the older master's style, that even Stravinsky later claimed not to remember exactly which bits were whose. But while few will fail to recognise the nostalgic yearning of Tchaikovsky's 'None but the Lonely Heart', which underscores the climax of the ballet's penultimate scene, there's also no mistaking the uniquely Stravinskian sense of glacial stasis and crystalline Classicism that sets in as the Ice Maiden rises slowly up through the cold, clear, blue waters of the lake to claim Rudy as her own during the concluding 'Lullaby of the Land beyond Time and Place'.

boy was forced under the scaffold by his parents in order to drink a bowlful of fresh blood as a cure for his stroke. Andersen's stories often mix a sense of such everyday cruelty with his own yearning for love and recognition. This combination of opposites together with his extraordinary imagination proved a winning formula, keeping his work popular long after literary fairy tales by Ruskin, Thackeray, George MacDonald and others have become museum pieces. For while young readers can always warm to occasional glimpses of horror in their literature, most of them have little time for the sentimentality that so many adult authors have always resorted to when writing for a juvenile market.

Traditional fairy tales were originally part of an all-age oral culture and the folklorists who first collected them had no idea of publishing them for popular consumption. But, once these stories were in print, children fell on them, delighting in tales that reflected a truly wide range of feelings, characters and happenings, both positive and negative, and that were often full of wish-fulfilling fantasies that satisfied their wildest dreams of personal wealth and success. Children could identify with young heroes or heroines who would usually end up putting all potential rivals, including fellow family members, firmly in the shade. And, in contrast to the Sunday-school tracts and other moralising books with which they were force-fed, the leading characters of these tales were not always impossibly good: sometimes they were unworthy tricksters or lazy good-for-nothings, and yet, mostly, they still won the ultimate prize.

Andersen well understood the power of traditional fairy tales, self-selected to survive, long before the arrival of print, by those

ABOVE
Igor Stravinsky:
1915 portrait
by Jacques-Emile Blanche

LEFT
Theatre stage with
ballerinas: one of the
thousands of paper cut-outs
that Andersen used to make
while telling his tales

akg-images/Erich Lessing (above); Hans Christian Andersen Museum, Odense (left)

RIGHT
Anatol Lyadov: the man who should have written *The Firebird*

BELOW
David Drew as Kashchey in the Royal Ballet's 2001 revival of *The Firebird*, the score for which Diaghilev commissioned from Stravinsky after Lyadov failed to deliver

BOTTOM
Danny Kaye in the 1952 Frank Loesser-scored film musical *Hans Christian Andersen*

who remembered the best of them and then handed them on to the next generation. Three of the four stories in his first collection for children were based on folk tales, salty enough to raise problems when first published in Britain. (One worried translator of *Little Claus and Big Claus* tried to explain away the presence of the randy sexton at the farmhouse during the husband's absence by telling his young readers that 'he happened to be first cousin to the farmer's wife, and they were old playmates and good friends'.) But Andersen's fourth story was not only entirely original, it also avoided any moral lesson and addressed itself directly to its readers in plain, almost conversational language. Later tales brought in contemporary objects as characters, breaking away from the rural settings of traditional folk tales. An animated shirt-collar falls in love with a lady's garter; hot irons, scissors and combs are given speaking parts, along with an old street-lamp and the brass knobs on some railings.

Other stories concentrate on emotions, in particular *The Little Mermaid* with its agonising tale of unrequited love, now thought to refer to Andersen's passionate homosexual feelings for his lifelong friend Edvard Collin. This story was conceived on hearing the news that the man he adored was about to get married. It has a pervasive sense of melancholy of the type that still remains largely taboo in modern children's literature, even though children have moments of

Anatol Lyadov (1855–1914)

Baba-Yaga; The Enchanted Lake; Kikimora

Notoriously lazy, prone to procrastination and severely self-critical, though much-loved by fellow musicians, Anatol Lyadov composed little, and what little he did compose consists mainly of miniatures, short piano pieces and variations on folk tunes or other composers' themes. Stravinsky, who got his big break when Lyadov characteristically failed to deliver the *Firebird* score that Diaghilev had originally commissioned from him, recalled him as being 'very strict with his pupils and with himself … working slowly and, so to speak, under a microscope', later adding (perhaps to salve his conscience) 'He was a short-winded, *pianissimo* composer and he never could have written a long and noisy ballet like *The Firebird*. He was more relieved than offended, I suspect, when I accepted the commission.'

Yet, like Rimsky-Korsakov, his sometime teacher and longtime colleague on the staff of the St Petersburg Conservatory, Lyadov possessed a real gift for orchestral colour, coupled with a penchant for the fantastic. 'Give me fairies and dragons, mermaids and goblins, and I'm thoroughly happy,' he once remarked, as can be heard in his three best-known orchestral scores – *Baba-Yaga*, *The Enchanted Lake* and *Kikimora* – all three based on Russian fairy tales, each a descriptive *tour de force*, and none lasting longer than seven or eight minutes.

Baba-Yaga and *Kikimora* (both given their UK premieres at the Proms, in 1906 and 1917 respectively) present a matching pair of whirlwind scherzos, the first a fantastical forest ride for the flying witch familiar from the penultimate movement of Musorgsky's *Pictures at an Exhibition* (which can be heard, in Ravel's orchestration, the next night), the second a darkly brooding, comically grotesque portrait of an evil household sprite, brought up by a magician in the mountains, rocked in a crystal cradle by a talking cat, who, when fully grown (with a head like a thimble and body like a wisp of straw), spends her days banging about the house, her evenings whistling and hissing, and her nights spinning cobwebs and cursing till dawn.

By contrast, *The Enchanted Lake* seems becalmed in timeless torpor and sensuous stillness, fed by Delian and Debussian streams, shaded by shimmering echoes of Wagner's 'Forest Murmurs' and stirred by occasional waves of *Tristan*-esque desire.

depression too and may want to find some reflection of this from time to time in the books they read. Another story, *The Steadfast Tin Soldier*, approaches moral nihilism when, at its climax, a little boy suddenly 'grabbed the soldier, opened the stove, and threw him in. The child couldn't explain why he had done it.' Joined in the fire by his great love, the paper-doll ballerina, the tin soldier is quickly reduced to ashes, and that's that.

Such Scandinavian gloom – with around three-quarters of Andersen's stories mentioning death at some stage – has occasionally been too much for readers in Britain, where fairy tales have traditionally gone in for more upbeat endings. But Andersen also had a genius for charm and humour. *The Princess and the Pea*, criticised at the time of publication as 'not only indelicate but quite unpardonable', is a perfect tale. Another one, *The Emperor and*

the Nightingale, is a compelling study of exoticism mixed with regret. But crowned heads do not always get off lightly, and another story, *The Emperor's New Clothes*, quickly became something of a comic cliché, particularly in political argument. How strange that such a brilliant and sensitive writer should so often have come over as a crashing bore to those who knew him. After one prolonged visit, a sorely-tried Charles Dickens stuck a card above his departing guest's dressing-table mirror: it read, 'Hans

Andersen slept in this room for five weeks which seemed to the family AGES.' Other acquaintances were even less complimentary.

Since Andersen's day, published fairy tales have turned progressively more whimsical. Once fairies were no longer widely feared – and Andersen's own mother truly believed in the reality of ghosts and trolls – the fairy tale became redundant as a way of trying to understand, and if possible contain, potentially dangerous magical forces. Pockets of belief remained in remote parts

ABOVE
'Of all my parents' friends I had a predilection for Ravel because he used to tell me stories that I loved ...' (Mimi Godebska): 1909 portrait of Ravel in pyjamas by Achille Ouvré

BELOW
The Sleeping Beauty, 1842, by Daniel Maclise

Maurice Ravel (1875–1937) *Mother Goose – suite*

Unmarried and childless, a dapper little man (only about 5ft 4in tall), Ravel never quite put away childish things, retaining throughout his life a love of fairy tales and mechanical toys. His earliest orchestral work, composed when he was 23, is the 'fairy overture' *Shéhérazade*, intended as the curtain-raiser to a never-written opera based (like Rimsky-Korsakov's symphonic suite) on tales from *The Thousand and One Nights*. Two operas followed: the first, *L'heure espagnole* – an 'adult' comedy set inside a Spanish watchmaker's shop – opens with a precision-timed cacophony of clockwork-powered whirring, ticking and clicking apparently recycled from an abandoned opera based on E. T. A. Hoffmann's tale of Dr Coppelius and his walking, talking, living doll; the second, *L'enfant et les sortilèges*, is a magical cautionary tale about a naughty boy whose nursery toys all come to life to punish him – among them, an adorable fairy-tale princess, the child's 'first love', whose fate he will now never discover from the torn pages of his bedtime storybook.

But Ravel's most extended voyage through the realms of childhood fantasy remains *Mother Goose*, the suite of five 'pièces enfantines' that he originally composed, in 1910, as a piano duet for 11-year-old Mimi Godebska and her brother Jean, though the work is now more often heard in the orchestral version he made a year later.

Here he encapsulated his love for the classic French fairy-tales of Charles Perrault and Madame d'Aulnoy by retelling four of his favourites with a beguiling sophistication that belies any pretence of childish simplicity. First we spy on the Sleeping Beauty, who – like that other famous Ravelian princess, long since sleeping the sleep of the dead – dances a dreamy Pavane; next comes Petit Poucet (our Tom Thumb), whose wandering trail of breadcrumbs is soon snapped up by chirruping birds; he's followed by Laideronnette (or Little Ugly), the Empress of the Pagodas, who goes to her bath accompanied by a percussive processional of Chinese 'chopsticks' patterns and gong-like celesta notes that echo the gamelan orchestras Ravel had heard at the 1889 Paris Exposition; then we watch as Beauty waltzes round the Beast (and gradually transforms him from a growling contra-bassoon into a graceful cello); and the whole suite ends in a final breathtaking vista of 'The Fairy Garden', an achingly tender *adieu* to the lost world of 'Once upon a time ...'

24

Mary Evans Picture Library (right); Lebrecht Music & Arts (inset right); akg-images (below)

LEFT

Charles Perrault (1613–88): France's premier collector of fairy tales

RIGHT

Fairies at the bottom of her darkroom: Frances Griffiths in one of the faked photos that convinced Arthur Conan Doyle, among others, of the existence of the so-called Cottingley Fairies

INSET RIGHT

Paul Dukas, perfectionist composer of *La Péri*

BELOW

The Brothers Grimm, cleaning up fairy tales for childish consumption: double portrait (1855) by Elisabeth Jerichau-Baumann

of Europe, and there were always odd middle-class eccentrics like Arthur Conan Doyle or W. B. Yeats who still insisted on the truth of fairies. But for the most part these sprites joined other traditional bugbears and once-genuine threats, such as pirates, highwaymen and smugglers, in being safely sanitised within a growing urban culture and increasingly trotted out only as entertainment for children.

Following the same pattern, those fairy stories collected by the Brothers Grimm and other anthologists steadily became more anodyne with each revised edition: tales about incest or adultery were either dropped or else tactfully rewritten, with rejecting or abusive parents turned into wicked stepmothers and stepfathers. Literary fairy stories meanwhile abandoned the self-sufficient, occasionally untrustworthy fairy in favour of what Kipling contemptuously described as 'little buzzflies with butterfly wings and gauze petticoats, and shiny stars in their hair, and a wand like a school-teacher's cane for punishing bad boys and rewarding good ones'. No longer at home in forests or the untamed countryside, these fairies now belonged more properly to the bottom of a suburban garden.

In art, mean and menacing fairies can still be found in the pictures of Richard Dadd, who spent 43 years in mental institutions after inner voices told him to murder his father. Painted in minute detail, sometimes using a brush made of only a single hair, his masterpiece, *The Fairy Feller's Master-Stroke*, still conveys a sense of both eroticism and torment. A similar sense of darkness can be found in Henry

Paul Dukas (1865–1935) *La Péri*

A contemporary and friend of Debussy, and mentor of Messiaen, Dukas was, like Lyadov, a master orchestrator but a self-critical perfectionist who (doubtless inhibited by the high standards he set as a teacher, editor and critic) published little in his lifetime and destroyed most of his unpublished manuscripts shortly before his death rather than surrender them to the judgement of posterity.

Now known almost exclusively for his orchestral showpiece *The Sorcerer's Apprentice* (and even that largely thanks to Disney's Mickey Mouse-ification of it in *Fantasia*), Dukas's slight *oeuvre* comprises just 12 titles, including an early overture to Corneille's *Polyeucte*, a C major Symphony, two ambitious piano works – a set of *Rameau Variations* and a Sonata in E flat minor (hailed by Cortot as among the boldest attempts 'to adapt Beethovenian characteristics to the French style') – and two theatre works: the full-length opera *Ariadne and Bluebeard*, based, like Debussy's *Pelleas and Melisande* (from which it quotes) on a play by Maeterlinck, and

the short fairy-tale ballet (or rather 'poème dansée') *La Péri*, commissioned by Diaghilev for his Ballets Russes in 1911 (though never danced by them after Diaghilev refused to cast Dukas's 'rotund' mistress in the title-role).

The Peri of the title is a Persian fairy from whom Prince Iskender tries to steal the Flower of Immortality while she sleeps. But no sooner has he plucked the blossom from her breast than she awakes, seduces it back from him and then disappears, leaving him to the fate of all mortals. Effectively a 20-minute *pas de deux*, spun in a single arc of sinuous arabesques and continually evolving variations on two themes (the Prince's and the Peri's), and climaxing in a central ecstatic dance, Dukas's score melds the exotically magical soundworld of Rimsky-Korsakov's *Sheherazade* and Stravinsky's *The Firebird* with a natural Gallic grace and fondness for filigree textures. Shortly before its 1912 premiere, however, Dukas added an opening brass Fanfare, whose inflexible, block-like chords offer a curiously stern summons to the fairy-tale fantasy to follow.

Gustav Mahler (1860–1911) *Das klagende Lied (original version)*

Begun when he was just a student of only 17, Mahler's cantata *Das klagende Lied* ('The Song of Sorrow') is both the nearest he ever came to writing an opera and the kernel of all his future works. As he himself once said: 'All the "Mahler" whom you know was here revealed at a single stroke.' Yet this 'fairy tale from my youthful days' was also, in Mahler's punning words, his 'child of sorrow' – a score that was still critically derided at its belated 1901 premiere, despite the many revisions Mahler had made since it failed to win the Beethoven Prize 20 years before.

The chief casualty of these revisions was 'Waldmärchen' ('Forest Legend'), the first of the cantata's original three parts. It's there that we learn of the Queen who offers her hand to whoever first finds a red flower in the forest, of the two brothers who set out in search of it, and of how the younger finds the flower and sets it in his cap, only to be robbed and murdered in his sleep by his very own brother. Why Mahler cut it, at the same time deleting the titles of the other two parts – 'Der Spielmann' ('The Minstrel') and 'Hochzeitsstück' ('Wedding Piece') – isn't clear. Did the fratricidal murder perhaps remind him too powerfully of the death of his own beloved younger brother Ernst?

Either way, the tale is reprised in the next part of the cantata anyway, when a passing minstrel finds a whitened bone beneath a willow tree, fashions it into a flute and hears the murdered brother's voice emerge, singing his 'song of sorrow'. The climax of the tale is reached when the minstrel then appears at the wedding feast of the older brother and his queen, whereupon the bone-flute once again sounds its sorry song, the queen faints, the guests all flee and the castle crumbles into dust.

But if 'Waldmärchen' isn't essential to the storyline, its inclusion adds immeasurably to the work's musical impact, in which the influences of such early German Romanticists as Weber, Marschner, the Wagner of *The Flying Dutchman* and the Bruckner of the earlier symphonies all conjoin to offer a storybook vision of the German Middle Ages as seen through decidedly modernist eyes. And, amid all the exhilarating choral writing and poetic scene-setting, Mahler's personal imprint is everywhere to be heard, not least in the ironic use of the off-stage band during the feverish wedding festivities, the earliest example of that 'conjunction of high tragedy and light amusement' which Freud later identified as inextricably linked in the composer's mind. No wonder Mahler himself later observed, 'I cannot understand how so strange and powerful a work could have come from the pen of a young man of 20.'

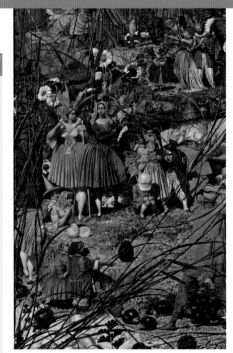

Fuseli's fairy paintings, and there are some uncomfortable goings-on in Charles Doyle's picture *The Fairy Lecture*. Father of Conan Doyle (and brother of fellow artist Richard Doyle), he too suffered from periodic insanity, in common with a number of other fairy painters. But on the whole, fairies in art became steadily more glamorised, posing prettily on the pages of Cicely Mary Barker's best-selling *Flower Fairies* books and reliable stand-bys on greeting cards.

In music, numbers of 19th-century composers grabbed the chance of getting their hands on so much ready-made atmosphere. Once again, a sense of transition is also evident, from the genuine mood of terror in Schubert's great song *The Erl King* to the charm of Mendelssohn's dancing fairies in his music for *A Midsummer Night's Dream*. Elsewhere fairies were rhapsodised by Tchaikovsky, made exotic

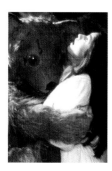

ABOVE
Nightmare in the nursery:
a childish bear hug is given
a new twist in a scene
from Neil Jordan and
Angela Carter's 1984 film
The Company of Wolves

RIGHT
'What thou seest when thou
dost wake, / Do it for thy
true-love take': *A Midsummer
Night's Dream* by Joseph
Noel Paton (1821–1901)

BELOW
The Fairy Tree
by Richard Doyle (1824–83)

by Rimsky-Korsakov and finally mocked in Gilbert & Sullivan's *Iolanthe, or the Peer and the Peri*. Some sort of comeback for giants, dwarfs, mermaids and sleeping beauties in Wagner's *Ring* cycle was no real compensation for the respect fairyland had by now lost, although Ravel's *Mother Goose* still makes a convincing case for the power and beauty of these old tales.

Today, fairies are having a renaissance. Tolkien has made elves and goblins respectable again, and Angela Carter has shown that rewritten fairy tales can still possess the unsettling energy of some of the older ones. In art, Peter Blake's portrait of Titania offers a striking break from Victorian sentimentality. At an academic level, fairy tales have been fair game for psychoanalysts ever since Freud wrote 'Does it not begin to dawn upon us that the many fairy tales which begin with the words "Once upon a time there was a king and a queen" simply mean "Once upon a time there was a father and mother"?' In *The Uses of Enchantment*, Bruno Bettelheim followed up the implications of this remark, making the case for fairy tales as psychic comforters. For him, the young storybook heroes who slay parent-substitute giants and the heroines who get the better of scheming mother-type witches provide deeply satisfying fantasies of vengeance to young readers with their own conscious or unconscious family scores to settle. The resolution of such fantasies remains guilt-free since all such action takes place within a story that in most other ways seems utterly divorced from real life.

Historians, meanwhile, are insisting on the realistic origins of some fairy tales, pointing out that there were indeed times when the young were sometimes abandoned if food was scarce and that step-parents did often take it out on children from previous marriages. Even cannibalism, a persistent theme in fairy tales, was sometimes known in times of famine. The occasional savageries

PROM
39

Felix Mendelssohn (1809–47)
A Midsummer Night's Dream – incidental music

Mendelssohn was only 17 when, in 1826, he composed his overture to *A Midsummer Night's Dream* – that youthful miracle of orchestral fantasy, with its scurrying, scampering strings, braying brass and undertow of romantic heartbreak, all framed within four unforgettable wind chords that unfold like a curtain gently rising and falling on a magical vision of fairyland. Equally miraculously, he was able to recapture all its youthful freshness and spontaneity of inspiration when, 17 years later, he was commissioned by the King of Prussia to write a complete set of incidental music for Shakespeare's play and composed a further 12 numbers, ranging in length from the briefest cues for entrances and exits to fully-fledged entr'actes and a finale.

Daringly, he supplied no music at all for the first of the play's five acts, but as soon as the action shifts from the city of Athens to the enchanted wood beyond, both the magic and the music begin. And, for anyone who only knows the ubiquitous Wedding March, the full score offers many other musical riches, from the quicksilver Scherzo that opens Act 2 and serene, horn-led Nocturne that closes Act 3 to the marvellously proto-Mahlerian mock Funeral March for Pyramus and Thisbe and comically clownish Bergomask that rounds off the rude mechanicals' play.

See also 'The Fairy Queen', page 68

Vítězslav Novák (1870–1949) *Eternal Longing*

PROM 50

Hans Christian Andersen's *What the Moon Saw* consists of 33 'evenings' on each of which the Moon visits a poor young artist in his garret to tell him of something he saw on his travels around the world the night before. 'But what I have given here are only hasty sketches,' the youth (or rather Andersen) confesses: 'A highly gifted painter, a poet or a musician might perhaps make more of them.' One artist who rose to that challenge was the Czech composer Vítězslav Novák, a pupil of Dvořák, whose tone-poem *Eternal Longing* (completed in 1905) faithfully follows the contours of the tale told on the 28th evening.

While passing over an ocean, the Moon had seen a flock of wild swans flying past. Suddenly, one of them sank slowly down to the surface of the sea, too tired to fly any further. And there it rested, 'as still as a white lotus blossom on a tranquil lake', until, with the first light of dawn, 'the swan soared aloft again, with renewed vigour, and flew towards the rising sun, towards the faint blue coastline where the aerial caravan had been heading. But now he flew alone, with longing in his breast. Solitary, he flew over the swelling blue waters.'

For Andersen, the ugly duckling turned solitary swan, the story was clearly autobiographical. For Novák, it was to prove almost prophetic. A shy, withdrawn child from a poor family who grew into a self-critical, doubt-ridden adult, he had struggled hard to put himself through the Prague Conservatoire and even harder to forge a truly personal style, which he finally did by lacing his predominantly Straussian, late-Romantic language with authentic Moravian folk idioms. Yet, no sooner had he attained wide national recognition, in the years immediately following *Eternal Longing*, and real material success (a publishing contract, a professorship, marriage to a former pupil) than he seems to have gone into a sudden decline. Cast in the role of old-fashioned reactionary by the sudden rise of the more authentically Czech and audibly modernist (albeit far older) Janáček, he spent the next 30 years treading water in the shallows of academe, before, like Andersen's swan, enjoying a late burst of creative resurgence, in the years immediately before and during the Second World War, with a series of works whose use of Hussite militant chorales and other Czech nationalist themes identified them unmistakably as calls to patriotic resistance.

Nikolay Rimsky-Korsakov (1844–1908) *Sheherazade*

PROM 57

Given its UK premiere by Henry Wood during the Winter Proms season of 1896, Rimsky-Korsakov's *Sheherazade* was inspired by the most famous collection of Eastern tales, *The Thousand and One* (or *Arabian*) *Nights*. These supposedly comprise the bedtime stories told each night by the Sultana Sheherazade to seduce her misogynous husband, the Sultan Shahriar, into postponing her promised execution the following dawn. The composer denied that any particular tales were depicted, and even withdrew the original movement titles in an attempt to have the piece appreciated as pure symphonic music. Yet the stern trombone theme at the start surely represents the implacable Sultan, while the sinuous solo violin arabesque that follows is unmistakably the voice of Sheherazade herself. In which case, what harm is there in invoking the images conjured up by those original movement titles – 'The Sea and Sinbad's Ship', 'The Story of the Kalendar Prince', 'The Young Prince and Princess' and finally 'The Festival at Baghdad, The Sea, Shipwreck, Conclusion' – especially since they serve to emphasise the all-pervasive swell of the sea, whose Shahriar-like power over life and death the composer knew all too well from his days in the Russian navy.

LEFT
Night flight: an aerial caravan silhouetted against a moonlit sky and sea (*Bewick's Swans over a Pearly Sea*, 1975, by Sir Peter Scott)

ABOVE
Home from the sea: 1898 portrait of Rimsky-Korsakov by Valentin Serov

BELOW
The *Galathea* at anchor in the port of Constantinople: a paper cut-out by Hans Christian Andersen

Alexander Zemlinsky (1871–1942) *The Little Mermaid*

Sexually confused and prone to repeated attacks of unrequited passion for people of both sexes (often in sibling pairs), Hans Christian Andersen once referred to himself as an 'amphibious creature', part male, part female, with a foot in both camps. How many of those who visit the statue of the Little Mermaid in Copenhagen harbour know that this 'amphibious creature', perhaps its author's most famous creation, is yet another of his tortured self-portraits, prompted by his lifelong love for Edvard Collin, a Danish civil servant? For the tale of the Little Mermaid – who pines from afar with a love that dare not speak his name, is prepared to walk on knives for the sake of her prince and is then forced to stand mutely by as he marries someone else – dates from the summer of 1836, when Andersen had fled back to his family home on the island of Fyn to avoid attending Edvard's wedding.

The myth of the water-nymph who can only win an immortal soul by winning the love of a mortal is an old and universal one: as *Undine* or *Rusalka*, it has been made the subject of operas by E.T.A. Hoffmann, Lortzing, Dvořák, Dargomyzhsky and others, while Tchaikovsky's *Swan Lake* is a balletic variation on the same theme. The uniquely personal twist to Andersen's retelling is that his mermaid eventually gains her eternal soul, not as a reward for winning a man's love, but as a consolation-prize for failing to do so.

Alexander Zemlinsky, whom his pupil and rumoured lover Alma Schindler (later Mahler's wife) once called 'almost the ugliest man I have ever seen' and whose Oscar Wilde opera *Der Zwerg* ('The Dwarf') is usually assumed to have had autobiographical associations, began his three-movement 'Fantasy after Andersen' in 1902. Although it doesn't slavishly follow the course of the story's narrative, the opening clearly represents the underwater kingdom (with the Little Mermaid herself portrayed by a forlorn little violin solo), followed by the storm and shipwreck and the mermaid's rescue of her unknown prince; the second movement then describes her visit to the Sea Witch, who magics her tail into legs at the cost of her tongue; while the third charts her time on earth, her failure to win the prince's love, and finally her transformation into an immortal spirit of the air.

Another of those highly self-critical composers who seem drawn to the childhood realm of fairy tale, Zemlinsky withdrew the score of *Die Seejungfrau* after its 1905 Vienna premiere. The first movement later got left behind when he fled to America after the Anschluss and the complete score wasn't heard again until 1984.

found in the Grimms' tales are not therefore simply psychological fantasies designed to fuel dreams of revenge within the imagination. In Nazi Germany, the violence in these stories, carried over from memories of the past, was later wilfully exaggerated in special editions of the Grimms' tales distributed to schools, in which it was often shown as directed towards various 'outsider' characters, mostly portrayed with a specifically anti-Semitic twist.

But, misused or not, fairy tales still get closer to certain human truths and needs than we may sometimes choose to admit. For such reasons, they remain the most fascinating of all stories, with Hans Andersen's tales an honorary literary addition to these remnants of an ancient folk culture that still refuse to disappear.

TOP RIGHT
A sting in the tail: Edvard Eriksen's 1913 statue of *The Little Mermaid* in Copenhagen harbour

BELOW
Alexander Zemlinsky, whose symphonic fantasy after Andersen's tale languished unperformed for 80 years

'Fairy Tales' in music at the Proms 2005

Berlioz	Romeo and Juliet	Prom 23
Dukas	La Péri	Prom 28
Lyadov	Baba-Yaga; The Enchanted Lake; Kikimora	Prom 15
Mahler	Das klagende Lied	Prom 33
Mendelssohn	A Midsummer Night's Dream – incidental music	Prom 39
Musorgsky	Pictures at an Exhibition (orch. Ravel)	Prom 16
Novák	Eternal Longing	Prom 50
Purcell	The Fairy Queen	Prom 3
Ravel	Mother Goose – suite	Prom 16
Rimsky-Korsakov	Sheherazade	Prom 57
Sørensen	The Little Mermaid	Prom 38
Stravinsky	The Fairy's Kiss	Prom 15
	The Firebird – suite (1945)	Prom 50
	The Nightingale	Prom 8
Tchaikovsky	Iolanta; The Nutcracker – excerpts	Prom 42
	The Snow Maiden – excerpts	Prom 19
Tippett	The Tempest – suite	Prom 70
Wagner	Die Walküre	Prom 4
Zemlinsky	Die Seejungfrau	Prom 67

Are you listening?

The result of over 25 years of continuous development, Meridian has created the internationally-acclaimed **G Series** to deliver the ultimate audio-visual experience – in your own home.

From its superb sound and precision electronic design to the soft-key-based controls and luxurious glass and machined metal finish in silver or black; in stereo or surround; analogue or digital; the G Series forms the heart, soul and sound of your home cinema system. The ideal complement to Meridian DSP loudspeakers or conventional designs, the G Series needs more than a quick look – it deserves a serious listen.

The G Series. Visit your Meridian dealer, or ask your installer to specify Meridian. Sound and vision – for those who listen.

BOOTHROYD STUART
MERIDIAN©

Meridian Audio Limited
Latham Road, Huntingdon, PE29 6YE, UK
Tel: +44 (0)1480 445678 Fax: +44 (0)1480 445686
www.meridian-audio.com/bpg/

EDINBURGH INTERNATIONAL FESTIVAL

FESTIVAL 2005

'...IT DOES WHAT ALL FESTIVALS SHOULD BE DOING: TAKING CHANCES NOT POSSIBLE ELSEWHERE...'

THE FINANCIAL TIMES

From the first notes of the Opening Concert on Sunday 14 August to a final week residency by the Bamberg Symphony Orchestra led by Jonathan Nott, Edinburgh International Festival fills the city with world class music for three glorious weeks.

Festival 2005 includes the first British staging of John Adams's opera **The Death of Klinghoffer** alongside stagings of Britten's **Curlew River** and Messager's musical comedy **L'Amour Masqué**. There are concert performances of Mozart's **La Clemenza di Tito**, Wagner's **Tristan und Isolde** and Rossini's rarely performed **Adelaide di Borgogna**. Concerts include the Rotterdam Philharmonic Orchestra and Herbert Blomstedt; the West-Eastern Divan Orchestra led by Daniel Barenboim; Jiří Bělohlávek conducting Mahler's 9th Symphony; Tchaikovsky Symphony Orchestra of Moscow Radio with Vladimir Fedoseyev and Ingo Metzmacher leading the Gustav Mahler Jugendorchester. Recitalists include Alfred Brendel, Llŷr Williams, Magdalena Kožená and Hanno Müller-Brachmann.

And then there's an amazing programme of dance and theatre, ranging from Fedoseyev conducting the Tchaikovsky Symphony Orchestra for a new production of **Swan Lake** and Kwamé Ryan conducting the Scottish Chamber Orchestra for Scottish Ballet, to cutting edge contemporary dance, the complete plays of JM Synge and much more.

Browse the programme and book for all Edinburgh International Festival performances online at www.eif.co.uk or call 0131 473 2000 for a free brochure

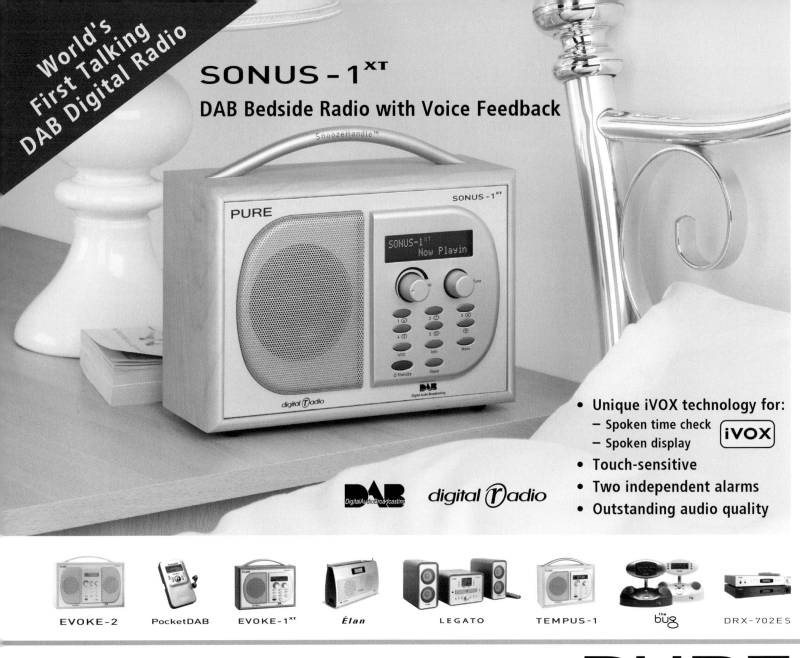

World's First Talking DAB Digital Radio

SONUS-1ᵡᵀ

DAB Bedside Radio with Voice Feedback

SnoozeHandle™

PURE

SONUS-1ᵡᵀ

SONUS-1ᵡᵀ
Now Playin

digital radio

Digital Audio Broadcasting

- Unique iVOX technology for:
  - Spoken time check
  - Spoken display
  iVOX
- Touch-sensitive
- Two independent alarms
- Outstanding audio quality

DAB
Digital Audio Broadcasting

digital radio

| EVOKE-2 | PocketDAB | EVOKE-1ᵡᵀ | *Élan* | LEGATO | TEMPUS-1 | the bug | DRX-702ES |

For an information pack or advice on digital radio (including reception in your area) please call 01923 277589   www.pure.com

PURE

World Leaders in DAB digital radio

ANNIVERSARY

COMPOSERS

MICHAEL TIPPETT 1905–98

A poet in a barren age: **Ian Kemp** profiles the visionary composer who intuitively responded to the darker side of human nature with music of abounding beauty and abiding hope

ABOVE
'God overpowered him – the child of our time': police photograph of Hershel Grynszpan, the 17-year-old German-Jewish refugee whose assassination of a Nazi embassy official in Paris precipitated the *Kristallnacht* pogrom of November 1938, which in turn inspired Tippett's great oratorio

RIGHT
'Here is no final grieving': Tippett photographed in 1982

Centenaries are occasions for evaluations, discoveries, elegant appraisals, self-serving opinions, mud-slinging – and none more so than in the case of Michael Tippett. Reactions to his music have veered wildly ever since the 1940s, when it first became clear that, whatever criticisms might be levelled at him, he was nevertheless a composer of substance. Sixty years later he is still controversial. Why is this so? You would think that for a composer who died at 93 only seven years ago the dust would have settled and he would have been either welcomed among the immortals of 20th-century English music or allowed to slip away into oblivion.

When he died, he was pretty well the age of the century. He didn't really want to live that long ('Never get old,' he would say), yet on his deathbed he bestowed a kind of benediction by uttering some words from his wartime oratorio *A Child of Our Time*: 'Here is no final grieving, but an abiding hope.' This was not a bid to cast himself in the role of a priest, but a last salute to his faith in humanity. And he had needed this faith, for the 20th century had witnessed a succession of evils of unparalleled brutality, despite its technological advances and despite, of course, those instances of human warmth, intelligence and endeavour that, for Tippett, gave meaning to life.

Some of the reasons why he divides opinion derive from his championship of those things special to him: pacifism, agnosticism, psychoanalysis, resistance to religious bigotry, support of the underdog (whether children, the unemployed, the poor, the persecuted, ethnic minorities, prisoners of conscience – the list is endless). As for the more private side of his personality, he was cultured, exceptionally intelligent, approachable, courteous, generous, entertaining. His public and private values complemented each other. They needed clear-sightedness and courage to uphold. They were the values of a man acutely aware of the world he lived in and, though criticised by some as cranky, portentous and even offensive, they may now be generally regarded as ahead of their time.

The often rather modish subject-matter and droll expressions in his operas have invited further, knowing criticism; but their librettos will eventually retreat into the background and leave the music

and drama to speak for themselves. Whether any of the criticisms I have mentioned have much to do with the substance of his music is a moot point. What I mean is that the most important thing of all to Tippett was the compulsion to write music. It was obsessive, and a relentless call on craft and technique. He organised his daily routine to accommodate this imperative, thereby giving free rein to a ruthless streak of egocentricity and space for his otherwise very sociable personality. And the most important question to the listener of Tippett's music is what it sounds like, rather than what he was like, extremely interesting though that may be. This year's Proms retrospective gives a marvellous opportunity to find out,

'The moving waters renew the earth. It is spring'
A Child of Our Time

encompassing as it does a wide range of his music, from the canonical *A Child of Our Time* of 1939–41 to his fourth and last symphony of 1976–7 – an appropriate conclusion since it covers a complete life-cycle, from birth to death.

Like many composers, Tippett reacted against his seniors, against what he then considered the boneless pastoralism of Delius, Vaughan Williams and Butterworth. Accordingly his early music draws its inspiration from the sustained and dense argument of the great classics and from the counterpoint and rhythms of his Tudor and Jacobean forebears. But his instinct was to reject nothing and he responded, for example, to folk song and jazz as well.

The most striking characteristic of his music is its exuberant view of life. Something of this is to be heard in *A Child of Our Time*, even if its dark subject-matter – the plague of persecution, and specifically the Nazi pogroms against the Jews – means that his most popular work is not his most characteristic. Another dark yet passionate work, also rooted in the tragedy of World War II, is the superb song-cycle *The Heart's Assurance*, written in 1951 for Britten's partner, Peter Pears (the tenor soloist in the 1944 premiere of *A Child of Our Time*). The outgoing, starry-eyed Tippett with his new and fresh re-creation of English pastoralism can be heard in the 'Ritual Dances' from his first opera, *The Midsummer Marriage* (premiered at Covent Garden in 1955) and in the Piano Concerto that he composed immediately after it, as also in the *Divertimento on Sellinger's Round* that grew from an Aldeburgh Festival commission for the Queen's coronation year. But the work that Tippett aficionados will look forward to most is undoubtedly

The Vision of St Augustine (a BBC commission, premiered at the Royal Festival Hall in January 1966) – an extraordinary conception that epitomises Tippett the composer, unafraid to change his style radically, prepared to take enormous risks and to take his performers to extremes: the composer who was indeed a visionary.

Tippett at the Proms 2005

A Child of Our Time	Prom 1
The Vision of St Augustine	Prom 14
Divertimento on Sellinger's Round	Prom 17
The Midsummer Marriage – 'Ritual Dances'	Prom 31
Piano Concerto	Prom 34
Symphony No. 4	Prom 47
Choral works	Prom 70
The Tempest – Suite	Prom 70
The Heart's Assurance	PCM 6
Piano Sonata No. 3	PCM 6

ALBAN BERG 1885–1935

Seventy years after the untimely death of Alban Berg, **Bayan Northcott** surveys the paradoxical nature of his musical legacy

ABOVE & RIGHT
Berg in the flesh *(above)* and in the portrait that his friend and teacher Arnold Schoenberg painted of him, *c*1910

'It is too horrible. One of us is gone, who anyway were only three, and now we two must bear this isolation alone. And the saddest aspect is it had to be the one of us who had had success, who could at least have enjoyed *that*.' So wrote Arnold Schoenberg from his Californian exile to his other favourite pupil Anton Webern back in Vienna on hearing of the untimely death at only 50 of Alban Berg on Christmas Eve 1935. Webern was equally overcome. Persuaded to conduct the posthumous premiere of Berg's Violin Concerto at the 1936 ISCM Festival in Barcelona, he broke down completely during the rehearsals, leaving Hermann Scherchen to convey the work to its deeply moved audience.

When Schoenberg wrote of Berg's comparative success, he was doubtless thinking primarily of the international impact of his first opera, *Wozzeck* (1917–22), with its oppressed protagonist driven to murder and suicide, following its triumphant Berlin premiere in 1925. But, at the time of Berg's death, and long afterwards, there was a general feeling that, of the three masters comprising the so-called Second Viennese School, his output was the least doctrinaire and most approachable.

It was not just that his music, even at its most dissonant, continued to harbour tonal allusions to fanfares and waltzes, ragtimes and Bach chorales. Whole chunks of it,

from the March of the *Three Orchestral Pieces*, Op. 6 (1914–15), to the final Adagio of his second opera *Lulu* (1929–35) – encompassing the murder of its *femme fatale* heroine at the hands of Jack the Ripper – could easily be heard as one step on from Mahler. And this despite the fact that *Lulu*, and indeed the Violin Concerto (the composition of which interrupted Berg's orchestration of the opera), used the dreaded 12-tone method. If Schoenberg, who devised the method, was the intellectual of the group and Webern the ascetic, Berg surely represented Viennese modernism with a human face.

Yet more detailed research has strikingly challenged this received view. It seems that Schoenberg's denial of intellectualism, his claim that he could scarcely compose 10 bars without inspiration, was probably true; certainly his output is strewn with abandoned fragments. And behind Webern's crystalline structures lay a deeply traditional Austrian Catholic pietism, finding allegorical confirmations in the patterns of nature.

Behind the surging romanticism of Berg's surfaces, by contrast, scholars have gradually uncovered layer upon layer of the most arcane devices. Even before Berg turned to 12-tonery, his scores were already riddled with secret ciphers referring to personages and events in his private life, and patterned by all manner of proportional and numerological schemes for pitch, rhythm,

barring, tempo and structure. Despite the charm and humanity he presented to the world, it turns out that Berg was the real intellectual of the Second Viennese School.

So how did he manage to fuse his innate feeling for his late-Romantic musical heritage with the labyrinthine calculations of his crossword-puzzle mind? In fact, it could be argued that he never did manage it, quite; that there remains an ambiguous, even occluded, element in his bar-to-bar musical language, as though its expressive and conceptual cogs are not always engaging exactly. This might seem an aesthetic failing. Yet it offered a uniquely potent medium for the themes of disquiet, unfulfilment and dissolution that preoccupied him from first to last.

In both of the operas, the characters seem helplessly trapped in repeating patterns of fate. So, in life, did Berg himself: the beautiful, gifted, aristocratic man with the seemingly ideal marriage, in fact hopelessly in love elsewhere, constantly undermined by money and health crises, and menaced by the catastrophic effects of world events. It is somehow emblematic that the Violin Concerto, written as a requiem for Alma Mahler's young daughter Manon Gropius, should turn out to be his own. Indeed, Berg's pupil, the music philosopher Theodor Adorno, wrote of his 'complicity with death' and alleged that his typical procedure was to conjure the most elaborate musical forms out of almost nothing – and then to allow them to disintegrate again into nothingness.

As perhaps was never more directly illustrated than by Webern. Twelve days after the Barcelona débâcle, he pulled himself together enough to conduct the second performance of the Violin Concerto, at a BBC invitation concert in London. A unique off-air recording survives (and has recently been released on CD). So hesitant is Webern's opening beat, the work threatens to fall apart almost before it has got under way. And, as the anguished finale gives up the ghost in terminal stasis, we seem to be hearing not just a requiem for Alban Berg, but for an entire culture.

ABOVE
Manon Gropius, the daughter of Mahler's widow Alma and the 'angel' to whose memory Berg's Violin Concerto was dedicated

FAR LEFT
The 22-year-old American actress Louise Brooks as Lulu in G. W. Pabst's 1929 film *Pandora's Box*, based on the once-banned Wedekind play that also inspired Berg's uncompleted second opera

LEFT
The Hungarian-Jewish soprano Rose Pauly as Marie, Wozzeck's murder victim, in the 1930 Vienna staging of Berg's first opera

'Alban Berg is an extraordinarily gifted composer … enthusiastic and uncritical, receptive of the beautiful whether old or new, whether music, literature, painting, sculpture, theatre or opera'

Arnold Schoenberg, 1910

Berg at the Proms 2005	
Three Pieces for Orchestra, Op. 6	Prom 33
Lulu Suite	Prom 44
Violin Concerto	Prom 55
Three Fragments from 'Wozzeck'	Prom 71

ARVO PÄRT born 1935

As he prepares to celebrate the Estonian composer's 70th birthday, choral director **Paul Hillier** reveals how Pärt's new simplicity was summoned into being by the sound of bells

ABOVE
Ringing in the new:
Arvo Pärt

Arvo Pärt's music has a sound that appears hauntingly simple, though it stirs complex emotions, and is immediately recognisable. Much of it uses voices singing sacred texts, and is composed in a style that communicates directly with audiences right around the world. But it wasn't always so. His earliest works, dating from the 1960s, were very different – mostly orchestral scores of passionate intensity, which seemed driven by despair and anguish beyond bearing.

Then came 1968, the year of student demonstrations across Europe, Soviet tanks rolling into Prague, and the escalating war in Vietnam. And this was also a year of crisis for Pärt. He wrote a work called *Credo* in which he used modern serial techniques to deconstruct the Prelude in C major from Book 1 of Bach's *Well-Tempered Clavier* and, after this work was performed in Tallinn, he virtually stopped composing for several years. Rejecting the style he'd been using, he began to study Gregorian chant (seeking to understand the timeless quality of its ebb and flow); he also studied medieval and Renaissance polyphony, and became fascinated too by the sound of church bells. From there he slowly pieced together the outlines of a new way of writing. It was as if he'd had an accident, and had to learn gradually how to walk again as a composer. Then in 1976 came the first pieces in a completely new style,

which he called 'tintinnabuli' (from the Latin word for 'bell'), and which has remained the basis of his music ever since.

One of the hallmarks of Pärt's 'tintinnabuli' music is its strong similarity on the page to early music: the refreshing lack of expression marks, its diatonicism, few if any accidentals, and a predominance of simple key signatures. Furthermore, the music appeared to be open to various realisations, so that the performer might use it in a number of different ways.

Although Pärt now scores his works very carefully, there remains the sense that the music could be realised by different combinations of voices or instruments and still retain its essence, as is often the case with Renaissance music. And there are other more obvious echoes of early music – the use of chant-like melodies, certain chordal progressions and cadential figures, and generally attending to the rhetorical structure of a text rather than dramatising its mood. The unifying feature of Pärt's music remains, however, the enduring use of the tintinnabulating triads that give his style its name.

Pärt at the Proms 2005

An den Wassern; Nunc dimittis; Salve regina; Trivium; Dopo la vittoria	Prom 45

GIACOMO CARISSIMI 1605–74

Graham Dixon celebrates the 400th anniversary of the Roman master whose music Pepys praised in his diary as 'the best … in the world'

When compared with Venice, Rome has had an image problem as far as Baroque music is concerned. At least, that is how many popular music histories have represented the situation. Apart from Giacomo Carissimi, Rome did not give rise to many figures who attained the importance of a Monteverdi or one of the Gabrielis. That Carissimi passed the test of acceptability in Venice is proved by the fact that St Mark's attempted to headhunt him on Monteverdi's death – a major compliment to someone from outside the northern sphere.

Carissimi, however, declined the opportunity to move north. Born in the small town of Marino near Rome in 1605, he spent a few years directing the cathedral music in Assisi before moving, in his mid-twenties, to a highly prestigious institution, the Jesuit-run Collegio Germanico (German College) in Rome, where he spent the remaining 45 years of his life.

Yet, though Carissimi stayed put, his influence spread widely. At the Collegio Germanico he drew students from all over northern Europe, as well as Charpentier from France. He composed church music, not in the old polyphonic style of the previous generation, but in a fashionable idiom for a small number of voices and continuo. His students carried this style across Europe when they returned home.

Carissimi's music was thus widely disseminated: even in his own time, manuscripts could be found in France and England, as well as Sweden. In later life, he was also court musician to the exiled Queen Christina of Sweden, who had abdicated and converted to Catholicism in 1653. For her academy of cultivated individuals, Carissimi composed much of his secular music, dramatic cantatas largely based on classical themes.

Carissimi's best-known music was written for the Oratory of the Most Holy

Crucifix, which employed a freelance musician each year to compose Lenten music. This was the preserve of Roman nobles, for whom music provided a diversion from the rigours of Lent. The themes of Lenten services are frequently dramatic; for this context Carissimi wrote his Old Testament settings – *Jonah*, *Jephtha*, *The Sacrifice of Isaac* – and dramatically reminded listeners of the impending *Last Judgement*. These oratorios are a curiosity, since this was the only Roman institution to demand Latin texts. As each narrative unfolds, Carissimi creates a series of miniature tableaux, delineated by tonality and texture, to encapsulate the drama.

Carissimi has enjoyed a long performance tradition in London. Writing in 1664, Samuel Pepys recalls an evening of music-making spent performing a work – then generally estimated to be 'the best piece of musique … in the world' – by 'Seignor Charissimi the famous master in Rome'. This is a very serious claim. Perhaps those who hear this season's Proms Chamber Music concert devoted to Carissimi will also feel that they have heard the best piece of music ever composed. In any case, bringing Carissimi's music – in his anniversary year – back to a city where he was so admired during his lifetime gives us all a chance to appreciate the vitality and drama of his output.

ABOVE
Jonah and the Whale by Giotto: fresco (c1305) in the Cappella Scrovegni, Padua

LEFT
The Academy of Queen Christina by Pierre Louis Dumesnil the Younger (1698–1781)

Carissimi at the Proms 2005	
Oratorio 'Jonah'; motets	PCM 7

THOMAS TALLIS 1505–85

Tess Knighton profiles the 16th-century composer who successfully straddled the Reformation, writing music for both the Latin and Anglican rites and enjoying the favour of successive English kings and queens of both faiths

ABOVE
Queen Elizabeth I: the so-called 'Pelican Portrait', c1574, by Nicholas Hilliard

RIGHT
Thomas Tallis: composer by Royal appointment

Like many of the great composers of the 16th century, Tallis the man remains something of an enigma. We have no record of his birth, although he was most probably born in 1505. The first step on an illustrious career seems to have been as an organist at the Benedictine priory of Dover; we don't know exactly when he moved to the church of St Mary-at-Hill, in London, nor precisely how long he was then a singer at Canterbury Cathedral. In 1577 he claimed to have served Elizabeth I and her predecessors 'these fortie yeres', although he doesn't seem to have served full-time as organist of the Chapel Royal until 1543.

What we do know is that he survived the religious upheavals of Reformation England, composing with equal success both Latin and English church music as was required of him, and that masterpieces such as his setting of the votive antiphon *Gaude gloriosa Dei mater* and his extraordinary 40-voice motet *Spem in alium* (once thought to have been composed for Elizabeth I's 40th birthday) continue to impress and move us today.

Tallis may have secured his position in the Chapel Royal through the support of Thomas Cranmer, Henry VIII's appointee as

Archbishop of Canterbury, and the religious reforms of the 1530s – spearheaded by Cranmer and his ally Thomas Cromwell, the king's vicar-general – led to a reversal of the highly elaborate, florid musical idiom cultivated by English composers in the pre-Reformation period. The effect on Tallis can be heard most clearly in Latin-texted works such as *O nata lux de lumine*, as perfectly

crafted as a miniature portrait of the period, and in his psalm settings and other pieces for the English liturgy. He contributed nine psalm tunes to Archbishop Parker's metrical Psalter of 1567, including one ('Why fum'th in fight') that was to be made famous not only through its inclusion in *The English Hymnal*, but also by Vaughan Williams who, captivated by the tune's unique blend of intimacy and grandeur, created one of his most inspired works, the *Fantasia on a Theme by Thomas Tallis*, in 1910.

Catholic, Protestant or pragmatist, Tallis enjoyed royal favour until his death in 1585, some 10 years before which Elizabeth I had granted him (and fellow member of the Chapel Royal, William Byrd) an exclusive licence to print music. The deep emotional currents running through such works as his settings of the Lamentations and *Gaude gloriosa Dei mater* suggest that he remained a committed Catholic; they also confirm his genius as a composer.

Tallis at the Proms 2005

Nine Tunes for Archbishop Parker's Psalter; O nata lux de lumine; Gaude gloriosa Dei mater; Spem in alium	Prom 64
Vaughan Williams: Fantasia on a Theme by Thomas Tallis	Prom 34

BBC SCOTTISH SYMPHONY ORCHESTRA
BBC SCOTTISH SYMPHONY ORCHESTRA
BBCSSO

CHIEF CONDUCTOR ILAN VOLKOV

"THIS ORCHESTRA HAS ALWAYS LOVED ADVENTURE…"
RAYMOND MONELLE, THE INDEPENDENT

THE BBC SCOTTISH SYMPHONY ORCHESTRA
ENTERS ITS 70TH YEAR BY RELOCATING TO AN
IMPRESSIVE NEW HOME IN GLASGOW'S
RESTORED CITY HALL. IN THE COMPANY OF
ILAN VOLKOV, AND COMPOSERS JONATHAN
HARVEY AND ANNA MEREDITH, IT WILL
CONTINUE ITS INNOVATIVE CONCERT SEASONS,
OUTSTANDING BROADCASTS AND ITS
GROUND-BREAKING LEARNING PROGRAMME.

JOIN THE CONTINUING ADVENTURE…
AT THE BBC PROMS, ON BBC RADIO 3, AND AT
GLASGOW CITY HALL.

BBC SCOTTISH SYMPHONY
ORCHESTRA
BBC.CO.UK/BBCSSO

NEW MUSIC

PROMS COMMISSIONS AND PREMIERES

Since the days of Henry Wood, the Proms have been committed to new music, premiering works by Schoenberg, Rimsky-Korsakov, Delius, Elgar and Bax, among others. This year the Proms presents 10 BBC commissions, 10 world premieres, six works new to the UK and five firsts for London, from the Cello Concerto by Scottish composer Stuart MacRae, still in his twenties, to a new song-cycle from the master orchestrator Henri Dutilleux, at the height of his powers aged 89. This year's Proms themes of the Sea and Fairy Tales are picked up in new works by Thea Musgrave and Bent Sørensen, and there's an exploration of the concerto, from composers as diverse as Michael Berkeley, John Corigliano, Marc-André Dalbavie and James MacMillan. **Lynne Walker** previews this year's new offerings.

HANS ABRAHAMSEN (born 1952)

Four Pieces for Orchestra
UK premiere

PROM 24

The *Four Pieces for Orchestra* by the Danish composer Hans Abrahamsen were born out of his idea of adding 'all the colours and textures of a big late-Romantic orchestra' to four movements from a set of earlier piano studies. The pieces are, he says, 'music of dreams and mourning', the outer movements slow, almost to the point of not moving. In marked contrast, the fast and forceful second piece creates a drama with its 'emotional and motional power.'

Abrahamsen exerts a masterly control over a vast orchestra of some 107 players – including Wagner tubas, mandolin, guitar and synthesizer – and looks upon Ilan Volkov, the dynamic young conductor of the BBC Scottish Symphony Orchestra, as the 'ideal' conductor for the occasion (the first time Abrahamsen's music has been played at the BBC Proms).

For his part, Volkov is fascinated with the *Four Pieces*, in which he senses 'a world inside the score'. He is astonished at the music's fragile and intimate qualities, at how intricately and delicately the notes are spun, and at the kaleidoscopic effect of its ever-changing focus.

THOMAS ADÈS (born 1971)

Violin Concerto
UK premiere

 PROM 69

Thomas Adès has rapidly become an exceptionally popular guest at the BBC Proms, whether as 'an absolutely brilliant composer and remarkable pianist', as *Le Figaro* described him, or as a 'fiendishly intelligent' conductor. Following the delight and excitement aroused by the premiere of his magical opera *The Tempest* at the Royal Opera in 2004, his seventh work to be heard at the Proms is eagerly anticipated.

Adès, who has long wanted to write a Violin Concerto tailored to the expressive scope and stylish perfection of Anthony Marwood's playing, will conduct his new work with the Chamber Orchestra of Europe, which represents 15 nationalities among its 50 members.

The dazzling orchestral work *Asyla*, with which Adès made his Proms debut as conductor/composer in 1999, went on to tremendous success, while his New York Philharmonic millennium commission *America: A Prophecy* made a big impact on Proms audiences in 2002. After *The Tempest*, which was acclaimed in the *Guardian* as 'a personal triumph and a public milestone' (winning the 2005 Olivier Award for Outstanding Achievement in Opera), Adès was hailed in *The New Yorker* as 'the major artist that his earliest works promised he would become'.

MICHAEL BERKELEY (born 1948)
Concerto for Orchestra
BBC commission: world premiere

PROM 5

Michael Berkeley's showpiece has grown out of his warm relationship with individual players of the BBC National Orchestra of Wales, of which he is Composer in Association, and his feeling for their musical personalities.

The slow movement, 'Threnody for a Sad Trumpet', was, Berkeley says, 'partly inspired by the orchestra's exceptional principal trumpet, Philippe Schartz, who has

often asked me to compose a piece for him.' He adds, 'As I was working on that movement the South-East Asia tsunami occurred. The depth of the tragedy was really brought home to me by the sad loss of Jane

Attenborough (with whom I had worked briefly), her daughter and mother-in-law. So this Threnody is really an "In memoriam to Jane".' The work is dedicated to the orchestra's Principal Conductor Richard Hickox, with whom Berkeley has been associated since the premiere in 1983 of his oratorio *Or Shall We Die?* In the intervening years, Berkeley's music has undergone a considerable development, his language having become moulded into a tighter musical idiom.

His BBC Radio 3 programme *Private Passions* and television presentations reflect his very public passion for making a wide range of music accessible to as wide a public as possible.

UNSUK CHIN (born 1961)
snagS & Snarls
world premiere of new version

PROM 36

snag small difficulty or obstacle hidden, unknown or unexpected • rough or sharp projection, which may be dangerous • catch or tear on something rough or sharp
snarl speak in an angry bad-tempered voice • act or sound of snarling • confused state, tangle • become confused

This song-cycle for soprano, mezzo-soprano and orchestra draws on words from Lewis Carroll's *Alice in Wonderland*, the subject of Unsuk Chin's forthcoming opera. Since the first performance of *snagS and Snarls* last year (also conducted, as is this Proms performance, by Kent Nagano) this extraordinarily talented Korean composer has elaborated on the original cycle, adding two new songs for her Proms debut. Chin, who studied with Ligeti in Hamburg, now lives in Berlin where her Violin Concerto – recognised with the prestigious 2004 Grawemeyer Award – was recently conducted by Sir Simon Rattle.

JOHN CORIGLIANO (born 1938)
Violin Concerto, 'The Red Violin'
UK premiere

PROM 18

John Corigliano's stunning film-score for François Girard's 1999 film *The Red Violin* is a dark romantic vision of the journey of one precious violin across three continents and through the ages. According to the *New York Times*, 'Whenever the music swells in this extravagant time-travelling costume drama … *The Red Violin* begins to assume the intense emotional colours of John Corigliano's ravishing score.'

The American composer, whose exhilarating Clarinet Concerto received its London premiere from Michael Collins at last year's Proms, won an Academy Award in 1999 for his *Red Violin* score. He has an unerring sense of theatre and is one of the most conspicuously eclectic voices of today. 'If I have my own style,' he says, 'I'm not aware of it.' He has attracted global acclaim for his highly expressive and compelling voice as well as for his flexible technique.

The first movement of this concerto originally appeared as the *'Red Violin' Chaconne*, and was recorded by Joshua Bell for the film's soundtrack release. The 'big feel' of the *Chaconne* persuaded the composer to

expand it into a full-length concerto for Bell, who gave the world premiere with Marin Alsop in Baltimore. The work has also been performed across the USA, including by the Atlanta and Dallas Symphony orchestras, the Philadelphia Orchestra and the Los Angeles Philharmonic.

MARC-ANDRÉ DALBAVIE (born 1961)

Piano Concerto
BBC co-commission with The Cleveland Orchestra and Chicago Symphony Orchestra: world premiere

One of the most intriguing of present-day French composers, Marc-André Dalbavie is writing a cycle of six related works of which this Proms commission, a Piano Concerto, is a major part. As with some previous works, his inspiration for this cycle is a literary form, here the unconventional arrangement of chapters and fluidity of time and memory explored in William Faulkner's narrative *tour de force, The Sound and the Fury.*

Dalbavie's luminous and tactile music explores timbre and colour (his vibrant *Color* was given its UK premiere at the 2002 Proms) and, as well as drawing on the French spectral school of the 1970s and 1980s, he reinterprets the post-serial approach of Pierre Boulez and the New York minimalism of Steve Reich and Morton Feldman. Although at one time he considered becoming a piano soloist (painting is another of his talents), Dalbavie is relieved, he says, that his friend Leif Ove Andsnes will be bringing his 'round and powerful virtuosity' to the concerto. The rest of this ongoing cycle includes a quartet and a trio, as well as the skeleton of a solo piano work – echoes of which run through this concerto.

HENRI DUTILLEUX (born 1916)

Correpondances
London premiere

'One of the big personalities of French music, next to Olivier Messiaen and Pierre Boulez,' is how the 89-year-old French composer Henri Dutilleux was described by the jury which recently awarded him the 2005 Ernst von Siemens prize – the Nobel Prize of the music world. His song-cycle *Correspondances* plugs what he describes as 'a serious gap in my catalogue', music featuring a solo voice, 'the most beautiful instrument of all'.

The title of the work is based on an allusion to the poem of the same name by Baudelaire. But Dutilleux's song-cycle is based on texts – or 'letters' – by Prithwindra Mukherjee (an ode to Shiva), the Russian dissident writer Solzhenitsyn (to his great friends and supporters Mstislav and Galina Rostropovich), the poet Rainer Maria Rilke and by Vincent van Gogh to his brother Theo. The four movements are interspersed with brief interludes and favour a particular section of the orchestra, employing varying degrees of orchestral texture and colour.

'It is,' reported the *Guardian* of the work's UK premiere, 'impossible for Dutilleux to make an ugly noise.' 'Scintillating, surprising, moving,' said *The Times*, 'with enough subtleties to reward multiple hearings, *Correspondances* shows no weakening of Dutilleux's powers to enchant.'

DETLEV GLANERT (born 1960)

Theatrum bestiarum
BBC commission: world premiere

'I wanted to write a dark and wild orchestral piece, uncomfortable, unregulated, and free in every sense – emerging from dark dreams and desires,' says Detlev Glanert about his second Proms commission, *Theatrum bestiarum*. 'The ideas and gestures behind the work are associated with my forthcoming opera *Caligula*, based on the play by Albert Camus [about the mad Roman emperor].'

It's ideal raw material out of which to forge a myth of the absurd, though as Glanert observes, *Theatrum bestiarum* ('Theatre of Beasts') represents 'a glimpse into the inner soul of a monster of a type that humans are only too capable of being'. The piece is scored for a large orchestra with an organ 'whose role,' says the composer, 'is as a duetting partner rather than as a solo instrument'.

The German-born composer is fascinated by the Romantic past, viewed from a modern perspective, and admires Mahler's all-encompassing musical attitude ('the symphony must be like the world … embracing everything') as well as Ravel's glittering, artificial surfaces.

In 1996 Glanert's previous Proms commission, the dramatic Third Symphony, drew critical acclaim. This new work is conducted by Oliver Knussen, whose performances with the BBC Symphony Orchestra are always keenly anticipated.

SOFIA GUBAIDULINA (born 1931)

The Light of the End
UK premiere

PROM 49

Wherever the music of the Russian composer Sofia Gubaidulina is played, it strikes a chord in its atmospheric application of dramatic and often dark-hued instrumental colour to her intensely spiritual material. Gubaidulina was last featured at the 2002 Proms when her stunning version of the St John Passion enthralled listeners.

The Light of the End, for large orchestra, was commissioned by the Boston Symphony Orchestra which gave the first performance in 2003. It was conducted by Kurt Masur who now brings it to the Proms with the London Philharmonic. The Boston reviews praised the work for its 'gorgeous orchestration' and 'fascinating combinations of percussion'.

'One also sensed in the music something of the spiritual transcendence that may follow the storms of life,' wrote one critic, 'depicted in edgy dissonance.' The title comes from the bright sound of the antique cymbals that close this 24-minute work.

MORGAN HAYES (born 1973)

Strip
BBC commission: world premiere

PROM 55

'Strips … clear sections like strips of material; stripes … vertical and horizontal; stripped down … taking the orchestra to pieces using small sections from within the main body of instruments; strip back … gradually progressing towards greater simplicity.'

As Morgan Hayes points out, a piece of music is often derived from several origins. In the case of his first Proms commission the connotations of the word 'strip' fed, he says, 'almost mysteriously' into his new work.

One of today's most strikingly original young British composers, Hayes has been widely admired for his breadth of musical imagination. 'I was very moved by Yukio Ninagawa's production of *Pericles* at the National Theatre and wanted to aim for an equivalent fullness and sensuality in *Strip*.' Having in the past drawn inspiration from composers such as Bach, Rameau and Purcell, here Hayes has obliquely 'stripped in' an element from two 'viscerally exciting' Proms commissions from 1988 by his teacher Michael Finnissy and Gerald Barry. In addition, the distinctive timbre of wood-blocks and log drums makes reference to Louis Andriessen's *De Snelheid* and Richard Barrett's *Vanity*. It sounds as if *Strip* is going to be something of a tease …

TATJANA KOMAROVA (born 1968)

Tänze mit verbundenen Augen
UK premiere

PCM 5

Born in Belarus, the Russian composer Tatjana Komarova has written prolifically for piano, voice, choir, orchestra and the stage, as well as producing chamber music for various combinations of instruments. The daughter and wife of musicians – her father Vladimir Komarov is also a composer, her husband is the pianist Lars Vogt – she studied at the Moscow Conservatory. Many of her works have been performed worldwide, particularly *Triptychon* (1993) for cello and piano, which has been taken up by several cellists including Truls Mørk and Boris Pergamenschikow, and has been broadcast on BBC Radio 3. Her Piano Sonata, premiered in New York in 1992, is frequently performed while *Ungemälte Bilder* ('Unpainted Pictures') was premiered in Lucerne by the Belcea Quartet. This season Komarova is the featured composer in the Orchestre de Bretagne's 'Portraits d'artistes' series.

Tänze mit verbundenen Augen ('Blindfold Dances'), her latest work for solo piano, brings Komarova's fresh and distinctive voice back to the BBC Proms after her Proms debut in 2000. Commissioned by the Klangspuren Festival in Schwaz, Austria, the work was premiered by Nicolas Hodges. Lasting around 10 minutes, it is made up of three short pieces which are not dances in the classical sense, says Komarova, but 'inner movements of the soul'.

JAMES MACMILLAN (born 1959)

PROM 8

A Scotch Bestiary
BBC co-commission with Los Angeles Philharmonic:
London premiere

James MacMillan's association with the Proms goes back to 1990 when *The Confession of Isobel Gowdie* created a stir. His whimsical concerto for organ and orchestra *A Scotch Bestiary* is inspired by the human characteristics and foibles of the creatures of American cartoons.

MacMillan has ingeniously coupled characters and instruments in a dazzling score subtitled 'Enigmatic variations on a zoological carnival at a Caledonian exhibition'.

Following in a tradition of musical portraiture established by Elgar, Saint-Saëns and Musorgsky, 'The Menagerie, Caged' takes us on a promenade among human characters in animal guise, including the 'cro-magnon hyena', the 'ubiquitous queen bee' and the 'red-handed, no-surrender, howler monkey'. In 'The Menagerie, Uncaged' the animals are released and rampage in a freewheeling, through-composed fantasy.

STUART MACRAE (born 1976)

PROM 48

Hamartia (Cello Concerto)
London premiere

The world premiere of Stuart MacRae's Violin Concerto made a huge impact at the BBC Proms in 2001 for the combination of a lilting melodiousness with a radical approach to the relationship between soloist and orchestra. The London premiere of his *Hamartia* for cello and strings is eagerly anticipated. The solo part is taken by the sensational young Chinese cellist Li-Wei,

who already has a formidable reputation in the UK, having performed at the 2003 Proms.

Hamartia means 'tragic flaw', says the composer, 'an imperfection of body or character in the hero of a Greek tragedy … that ultimately precipitates his downfall.' Heroism and imperfection are set against each other in a series of confrontations and collaborations between the 12 instruments of the Scottish Ensemble, each of which has its own distinct part. The opposing factors, according to MacRae, are reflected in two main types of musical material: 'the elemental, often mechanistic chordal music of the ensemble, and the

more expressive, lyrical quality predominantly heard from the cello.' By the age of just 27 Stuart MacRae had been the focus of not one but two major retrospectives of his music – 'a sure endorsement,' noted *The Scotsman* in 2003, 'that he is well worth listening to'.

THEA MUSGRAVE (born 1928)

PROM 6

Turbulent Landscapes
London premiere

A new work by the leading Scottish-born composer now resident in the USA, based mainly on seascapes by J. M. W. Turner. For details, see 'The Sea', page 13

PAUL PATTERSON (born 1947)

PROM 31

Orchestra on Parade
London premiere

'It's a real, exotic orchestral showpiece for orchestra,' says British composer Paul Patterson of his five-minute *Orchestra on Parade*, of which the National Youth Orchestra of Great Britain gives the London premiere this season. 'It's similar in format to Britten's *The Young Person's Guide to the Orchestra*, but done in about a quarter of the time. It shows off the orchestra in a flamboyant way using one theme which is pushed through all the sections of the orchestra, so that young

listeners who are new to orchestras might be engaged by it.'

Throughout his career Patterson has written music for, or to be performed by, children, beginning with his setting in 1966 of the cautionary tale of Rebecca, and including his large-scale *Little Red Riding Hood*, which has been translated into seven languages, and attracted among its celebrity narrators Danny DeVito and Julie Walters.

ESA-PEKKA SALONEN (born 1958)

PROM 57

new work
BBC commission: world premiere

No less highly regarded as a composer than as a conductor, Esa-Pekka Salonen and his music make regular and welcome appearances at the BBC Proms. Among the many previous successes he has enjoyed here are the UK premieres of several orchestral pieces as well as, most recently, the London premiere in 2004 of his solo violin work, *Laughing Unlearnt*. This year, his strikingly brilliant compositional voice is heard at the Proms with, for the first time, a brand-new work.

As yet untitled, it is a short orchestral piece specially written for the World Orchestra for Peace, an ensemble of some of the world's top players, originally formed in 1995 by Georg Solti. After Solti's death the baton passed to Valery Gergiev under whose direction the orchestra made its memorable Proms debut with Shostakovich's *Leningrad* Symphony at the penultimate night of the Proms in 2000.

'Gergiev is an old friend whom I admire both for his tireless work as a musician and for his devotion to humanitarian causes,' explains Salonen. 'For a long time we have tried to be involved together with a new commission and this opportunity feels to me like the perfect occasion and context. Music is a universal language, it has no political leanings, and it effortlessly crosses barriers to reach people everywhere.'

BENT SØRENSEN (born 1958)

PROM 38

The Little Mermaid
BBC co-commission with Danish National Symphony Orchestra & Choirs/DR: world premiere

Bent Sørensen, one of today's leading Danish composers, has based his first Proms commission on the fairy tale *The Little Mermaid* by Hans Christian Andersen.

The story unfolds in three movements, 'Tempest', 'Silence' and 'Party'. A choir of girls' voices takes the role of narrator and of the little mermaid's sisters, and extracts from Andersen's diary are sung by a solo tenor.

Given that several of his works feature a Gothic interest in the beauty of death and decay, it's perhaps not surprising that *The Little Mermaid* ends with the very last words Andersen confided to his diary. 'In a sense,' says Sørensen, 'the piece forms the way to death for both Andersen and the little mermaid. It's gentle, ruminative music, softly restrained throughout and making great play with the pure sound of young voices.'

FRASER TRAINER (born 1967)

PROM 21

for the living (Violin Concerto)
BBC commission: world premiere

Written for Viktoria Mullova *for the living* takes its (strictly lower-case) title from a poem by Lemn Sissay, *Advice for the Living*, which has lots of drive, a dark energy and a real sense of pulse and rhythmic direction. These elements of the poem are carried over into the music, along with a structural technique. 'In the poem,' explains Trainer, 'Sissay takes the word "dead", repeating it in almost every line in different contexts and this mirrors what I had been doing in recent pieces, trying to change the musical landscape around short cells, riffs or tags.

'I greatly admire Mullova's playing. She commissioned a miniature violin concerto, *Knots*, from me in 2003, which she's also now recorded. In *for the living* the violin is amplified in order to match the soloist against the sound of the full ensemble, which is divided into three groups and includes two saxophones, two keyboards, two marimbas and two vibraphones.'

Fraser Trainer's *Line-Up*, a site-specific work for Southwark Underground Station, was praised in the *Guardian* as 'a piece of serious and complex modern music'. The composer has won success with three London Sinfonietta commissions, has worked on music education projects in the UK and abroad, and has been involved in the education event associated with this year's *Violins!!* day (see page 92), of which this concerto is part.

MARK-ANTHONY TURNAGE (born 1960)

PROM 73

From the Wreckage
BBC co-commission with Helsinki Philharmonic
and Gothenburg Symphony orchestras:
UK premiere

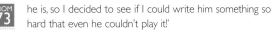

Mark-Anthony Turnage's latest work, *From the Wreckage*, came about as a result of a request from the trumpeter Håkan Hardenberger. According to the composer, 'I have worked with him before and know what a brilliant player he is, so I decided to see if I could write him something so hard that even he couldn't play it!'

'There is no narrative,' says Turnage, 'but it comes from a particularly dark moment in my life. It has a simple structure, with a very sombre opening on flugelhorn moving to trumpet then piccolo trumpet – as if the piece is being dragged up from the depths into the light. A big accelerando leads to a slower coda towards the end of the piece. And there are four percussionists surrounding the orchestra as if at the points of a compass, clicking (or ticking) time like a giant clock.

'It shadows a whole line of pieces that I have written in similar fashion – *Scherzoid* (for the New York and London Philharmonic orchestras) and the clarinet concerto *Riffs and Refrains*, which Michael Collins and the Hallé premiered this year – and this is the final one of its kind.'

HUW WATKINS (born 1976)

PROM 28

Double Concerto for viola and cello
world premiere

Huw Watkins's new work is a concerto for the unusual combination of viola and cello. 'There are no well-known precedents for the dark-hued, autumnal colouring produced by this particular pairing,' says the hugely talented young composer.

'The concerto is in three movements, although it does not follow any conventional pattern. Think of it more as new wine in old bottles! I've set myself a difficult task in wanting to write a direct, immediate piece that will sound as convincing in the Royal Albert Hall as on the Radio 3 broadcast.

'Being Welsh, I had my first experience of many orchestral pieces performed by the BBC National Orchestra of Wales in Cardiff. I also wrote my first orchestral piece, *Sinfonietta*, for the BBC NOW in 1999, and a Piano Concerto (2001–2) in which I took the solo piano role with this orchestra at its premiere. So I know their sound and their playing pretty well now.'

JOHN WOOLRICH (born 1954)

PCM 3

After the Clock
BBC commission: world premiere

'I want the contemporary music I listen to to be a mirror of the world I live in, with all its complexities, not an idealised reflection. If I could take any 100 years of music to a desert island, it would be the most recent. That way I'd get *The Rite of Spring* and [the Beach Boys'] *Pet Sounds*, Mahler's *Das Lied von der Erde*, Sibelius's Fifth Symphony, Billy Strayhorn's *Blood Count*, Berio's *Sinfonia*, Xenakis's *Jonchaies*, *West Side Story* and Shostakovich's Fourteenth Symphony. Not forgetting Debussy, the Beatles, Janáček, Kurtág, Frank Zappa, Sciarrino, Puccini and all the rest. What the last 100 years has given us is a fantastic, daunting, teeming diversity.'

So declared John Woolrich in the *Guardian* last February, revealing his fascinatingly eclectic tastes. A much commissioned and frequently performed composer, a highly creative teacher and an original programmer, Woolrich is an important figure in British musical life. His fascination with machinery and mechanical processes is reflected in his new chamber work *After the Clock*. 'I had in my mind the darkly comic world of Goya's paintings,' says Woolrich, adding that the music is 'dark but capriccio-like, comic with a shadow, featuring a ticking element and glowing lyrically towards the end'.

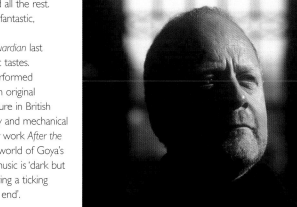

BBC
Symphony
Orchestra

The BBC Symphony Orchestra – seventy-five years of world-class performances, leading the way in creating new music

Join the celebrations as the BBC Symphony Orchestra and Chief Conductor Designate Jiří Bělohlávek mark the BBC SO's 75th anniversary with a season of exciting and distinctive concerts.

The BBC Symphony Orchestra: The Orchestra of the 21st century

Flagship Orchestra of the BBC Proms Associate Orchestra of the Barbican

All concerts in the BBC Symphony Orchestra's 2005-06 Barbican season are on sale now.

Visit www.bbc.co.uk/symphonyorchestra for full details and to book your tickets.

Call the Barbican Box Office from June for a free season brochure.

BBC RADIO 3 90-93 FM

020 7638 8891 Box office
Reduced booking fee online
www.barbican.org.uk

barbican

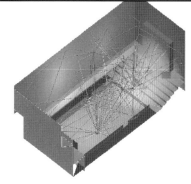

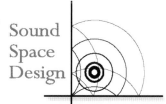

PHOTOGRAPHY MIKE HOBAN

GLYNDEBOURNE
ON TOUR 2005

W A MOZART
Le nozze di Figaro

A revival of the 2000 Festival production

G ROSSINI
La Cenerentola

A new production from the 2005 Festival season

J LUNN
Tangier Tattoo

A world premiere for the 2005 Tour

GLYNDEBOURNE	11 – 29 OCTOBER
WOKING	01 – 05 NOVEMBER
NORWICH	08 – 12 NOVEMBER
MILTON KEYNES	15 – 19 NOVEMBER
PLYMOUTH	22 – 26 NOVEMBER
STOKE-ON-TRENT	29 NOV – 03 DECEMBER
OXFORD	06 – 10 DECEMBER
EDINBURGH	13 – 17 DECEMBER

To join our FREE mailing list and receive full details of the 2005 Tour,
please call 01273 815 000 or email info@glyndebourne.com
or write to: GOT Mailing List, Freepost BR (235),
Glyndebourne, Lewes, East Sussex BN8 4BR

For full details please visit **www.glyndebourne.com**

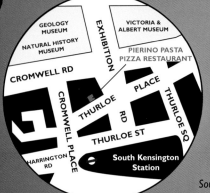

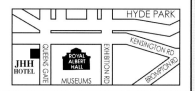

Conceived and designed by Marks Barfield Architects

Front row seats

Indulge yourself with a Champagne Flight on the British Airways London Eye. Savour a glass of Laurent-Perrier Champagne served by your host whilst you take in the spectacular views, night or day. We also offer a wide range of great value restaurant deals.

Visit ba-londoneye.com and book online to save 10%. Or call +44 (0) 870 5000 600.

BRITISH AIRWAYS
London eye

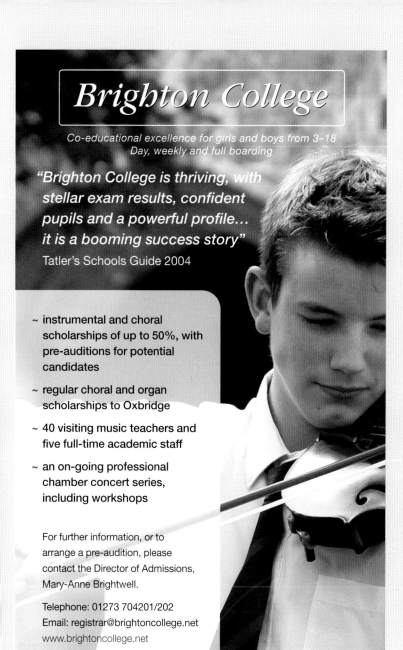

SEASON HIGHLIGHTS

GILBERT & SULLIVAN: HMS PINAFORE

Graeme Kay summons you aboard *HMS Pinafore*, the very model of a maritime operetta and the perfect centrepiece to an evening of Gilbert & Sullivan in this, our 'Sea' season

The work that launched Gilbert and Sullivan's transatlantic career (and more recently received the all-American accolade of being parodied on *The Simpsons*), G&S's sunny celebration of Britain's umbilical relationship with the sea is not only among the most deservedly popular of all their works, but also includes (as befits the reputation of Jolly Jack Tars) the only swear word to be found in the published text of the Savoy operas. The maritime subject virtually suggested itself: W. S. Gilbert was the son of a naval surgeon and claimed even more venerable nautical credentials through an alleged connection with an Elizabethan navigator, Sir Humphrey Gilbert, who planted the flag of English colonialism in North America in 1583.

In the current political climate, we might have cause to reflect on that particularly oracular G&S creation, Sir Joseph Porter KCB, First Lord of the Admiralty, and his notable confession: 'I always voted at my party's call, / And I never thought of thinking for myself at all.' The character was in fact based on William Henry Smith, founder of the eponymous newsagents' chain, who had risen from humble beginnings selling newspapers at railway stations to an appointment as First Lord of the Admiralty in the Disraeli Government. Smith was a landlubber but, as Sir Joseph observes in his patter song, 'Stick close to your desks and never go to sea, / And you all may be Rulers of the Queen's Navee!'

HMS Pinafore's bumboat woman, Mrs Cripps (aka Little Buttercup), has her origins in a character in Gilbert's *Bab Ballads*: Poll Pineapple. When Sullivan's music came out of copyright in 1950, Charles Mackerras, then a staff conductor at Sadler's Wells (and a lifelong devotee of G&S since his days as a young oboist in a Sydney theatre during World War II), proposed creating a ballet score based mainly on music from the Savoy operas. Choreographer John Cranko suggested a scenario built round Poll and her love for valiant Captain Belaye of HMS *Hot Cross Bun*. The resulting ballet – set to Mackerras's witty and breathtakingly seamless arrangement

of Sullivan scores – should make a perfect prelude to his performance of *Pinafore* itself.

And what better item to open the concert than the noble overture to *The Yeomen of the Guard*, one of the scores Mackerras mined for *Pineapple Poll*? The completed work was G&S's most conspicuous nod in the direction of Grand Opera – yet, like Sir Joseph Porter, it too had humble beginnings. Gilbert, waiting for a train at Uxbridge Station, had spotted a poster for a furniture company featuring a beefeater and the Tower of London and had determined to fashion it into a plot for a 'romantic and dramatic piece'. Sullivan, who was in the habit of farming out his operetta overtures to arrangers, composed the *Yeomen* overture himself – in a three-day frenzy of creativity during the last week of rehearsals for opening night on 3 October 1888. Symphonically conceived, the overture evokes Sullivan's own training in the Mendelssohnian tradition of the Leipzig Conservatory every bit as strongly as it expresses the bitter-sweet atmosphere of the operetta itself.

For more maritime music at the Proms, see pages 4–13

For more maritime music at the Proms, see pages 4–13

PROM 2 — **GILBERT & SULLIVAN**
HMS Pinafore, etc
Saturday 16 July, 7.30pm

ABOVE
Characters from *The Yeomen of the Guard* and *HMS Pinafore*, as pictured on Player's cigarette cards of the 1870s and 1880s

RIGHT
A scene from *HMS Pinafore* recreated in the 1953 Frank Launder and Sidney Gilliat biopic *The Story of Gilbert and Sullivan*

PURCELL: THE FAIRY QUEEN

As **Lindsay Kemp** explains, Purcell took no half-measures in turning Shakespeare's *Dream* into a Restoration 'semi-opera'

Shakespeare was not always the revered figure he is today, even in England. In 1662 Samuel Pepys declared after a rare performance of *A Midsummer Night's Dream* that it was 'the most insipid, ridiculous play I ever saw in my life', and there seems to have been little sense of outrage 30 years later when it next resurfaced in London in a version which, were it to hit the stage today, might well rejoice in the title *Dream: The Musical*.

In fact, Purcell's *The Fairy Queen* was just the kind of thing London audiences in the 1690s wanted: a spectacular musical play, with fine costumes, lavish sets, ingenious stage machinery and a big cast of singers, actors, dancers and instrumentalists. 'Dramatic

operas' was how they were described, and *The Fairy Queen*, Purcell's third (following the successes of *Dioclesian* and *King Arthur*), scored a hit for the Dorset Garden Theatre, spoilt only by the fact that the production expenses all but wiped out the profits.

Today such pieces are usually known as 'semi-operas', a perhaps not entirely unprejudiced reflection of the fact that they are not 'full', in the sense of every word being sung. But there was nothing half-baked about semi-opera. Rather, it was a form that had happily developed into an entertaining and dramatically coherent means of expression in its own right, some two decades before through-composed opera found favour in London with the arrival of Handel.

Their internal logic was clear enough: the principal roles – in this case the familiar Shakespearian ones of Titania, Oberon, Bottom, *etc* – were taken by actors, while the music was performed by minor, sometimes even nameless characters. In *The Fairy Queen* this is where the anonymous adaptor's hand is most in evidence, in the shape of various additional scenes and characters, including a drunken poet, two rustic lovers (one in drag) and a pair of affectionate Chinese. Yet the various musical set-pieces and interludes are not just incidental; they are designed to reflect the emotions of the main characters and the overall atmosphere of the play. And when the music comes from not only one of Britain's finest composers but also one of the most powerful songwriters of all time, the result is as magical and memorable as anything in Shakespeare's enchanted masterpiece – and perhaps the greatest musical score produced by any English composer before Sullivan.

For more fairy-tale music at the Proms, see pages 20–29

ABOVE
Henry Purcell: chalk portrait attributed to John Closterman, probably dating from 1695, the last year of the composer's life

LEFT
Titania's Awakening (c1790) by Henry Fuseli

PROM **3**
PURCELL
The Fairy Queen
Sunday 17 July, 6.30pm

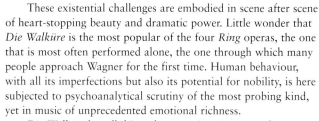

WAGNER: DIE WALKÜRE

As the Proms *Ring* cycle moves on to its second instalment, **Barry Millington** hints at the human truths that lie at the heart of this fairy-tale saga of Norse gods and heroes

ABOVE
Richard Wagner: portrait photograph, c1871

RIGHT
The Ride of the Valkyries by William T. Maud (1865–1903)

Given the fairy-tale elements of *Der Ring des Nibelungen* ('The Nibelung's Ring'), it is not altogether surprising that the stories of Hans Christian Andersen should have been bedtime reading for the Wagner children. The composer's wife Cosima noted in her diary with chauvinistic satisfaction that they much preferred the tales of the Brothers Grimm. Nevertheless Wagner himself had had a rewarding meeting with Andersen many years earlier, while he was working on the score of *Die Walküre*, when the two of them realised that they were kindred spirits.

Many of the fairy-tale motifs encountered in *Das Rheingold*, the first part of the *Ring* tetralogy – the giants, dwarves, mermaids, magic helmet and so forth – have disappeared by *Die Walküre* (though all are to return). The second instalment of the cycle, for all its heroic imagery, is rooted much more in social reality. On a soap-opera level we have bickering spouses, marital violence and extra-marital sex (with more than a touch of incest to keep up the ratings). But *Die Walküre* goes deeper and wider than this to engage with fundamental questions of human existence. Why are we here? To what extent is the accumulation of material possessions incompatible with humanity's finer instincts? Does the shadow of mortality ultimately exclude human happiness, or can the knowledge of the certainty of death shape our lives for the better?

The regime of Wotan and the other gods was already in decline at the end of *Das Rheingold*: compromised by deceitful bargains, their rule had surrendered its legitimacy. Now it's the turn of humans to attempt to govern their own existence without reference to supernaturalism. God is dead, or at least dying, and Man (and Woman) must take responsibility for his (or her) own actions.

These existential challenges are embodied in scene after scene of heart-stopping beauty and dramatic power. Little wonder that *Die Walküre* is the most popular of the four *Ring* operas, the one that is most often performed alone, the one through which many people approach Wagner for the first time. Human behaviour, with all its imperfections but also its potential for nobility, is here subjected to psychoanalytical scrutiny of the most probing kind, yet in music of unprecedented emotional richness.

Die Walküre has all this and even, at its stirring conclusion, a fairy-tale princess put to sleep on a rock surrounded by a ring of fire.

For more fairy-tale music at the Proms, see pages 20–29

PROM 4
WAGNER
Die Walküre
Monday 18 July, 5.00pm

BERLIOZ: ROMEO AND JULIET

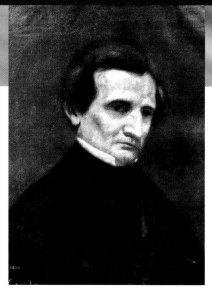

Gerald Larner reveals how Berlioz took Beethoven's 'Choral' Symphony as his model for translating Shakespeare's most lyrical love-story into the 'language of instruments'

Shakespeare's most lyrical play has generated much correspondingly lyrical music but, remarkably enough, not one great opera. There's Gounod's *Romeo and Juliet*, of course, but as a response to the challenge represented by the musical potential of Shakespeare's tragedy it pales into insignificance beside three non-operatic scores based on the same subject – Prokofiev's four-act ballet, Tchaikovsky's 'fantasy overture' and, the earliest and most inspired of them, Berlioz's 'dramatic symphony'.

Berlioz would not be surprised to learn that *Romeo and Juliet* still finds its most profound musical reverberations in the concert hall or ballet theatre rather than in the opera house. Having long intended to make an opera of it himself, when he finally settled down to write his *Romeo and Juliet* masterpiece he conceived the work as a large-scale choral symphony. This was not only because of his ambition to emulate Beethoven's Ninth but also because of his discovery of a fundamental truth about Shakespeare's poetic treatment of the relationship between Romeo and Juliet. 'The very sublimity of this love opens pitfalls for any composer who attempts to paint it,' he wrote in a preface to the score. So, he said, he 'gave his imagination greater freedom than the precise meaning of sung words would allow, turning instead to the language of instruments, a language richer, more varied, more flexible and by its very imprecision incomparably more powerful'. Only one of the characters in the play is given a voice – neither Romeo nor Juliet but Friar Laurence – and only in the choral finale.

If the symphonic structure of this *Romeo and Juliet* is not as clear as that of Beethoven's Ninth, it is because Berlioz has a story to tell. But while there are some daring formal innovations on the way to his choral finale, there are three purely orchestral movements roughly equivalent, though in a different order, to Beethoven's Allegro, Scherzo and Adagio. They are among the greatest of all Berlioz's inspirations – the brilliant Capulet ball scene with its dramatically engineered climax, the miraculously scored 'Queen Mab' Scherzo ('as thin of substance as the air') and, above all, a slow-movement equivalent of Shakespeare's balcony scene as melodious and as passionate in its instrumental discourse as any operatic love scene. Richard Wagner, who had the good fortune to be present at the first performance of *Romeo and Juliet*, at the Paris Conservatoire in 1839, was never to forget it.

PROM **23**

BERLIOZ
Romeo and Juliet
Sunday 31 July, 6.30pm

ABOVE
Hector Berlioz: 1850 portrait by Gustave Courbet

LEFT
Romeo and Juliet – The Balcony Scene, c1796, by John Francis Rigaud

TCHAIKOVSKY: IOLANTA

Andrew Huth on the unfamiliar Tchaikovsky opera that was premiered on the same night as *The Nutcracker* and was once rated even more highly

ABOVE
Pyotr Ilyich Tchaikovsky:
1893 portrait by Nikolay
Dmitryevich Kuznetsov

The Maryinsky Theatre in St Petersburg began the year 1890 with the premiere of *The Sleeping Beauty* and ended it by launching *The Queen of Spades*. With two such successes, they were naturally eager to have another work from Russia's favourite composer, but weren't sure whether to commission a new opera or a new ballet. In the event, they hedged their bets: Tchaikovsky was commissioned to provide a full evening's entertainment consisting of a one-act opera and a two-act ballet. At the first performance in 1892 the opera was generally preferred to the ballet, a judgement that seems very odd today, when *The Nutcracker* has become the most famous of all ballets and *Iolanta* is still one of Tchaikovsky's least-known works.

Like many of Tchaikovsky's operatic heroines, Iolanta is a fragile, suffering girl; but in this case she doesn't realise that there's anything wrong. She has been blind from birth, but has been so protected by her father that she is quite unaware of being different from other people. When the knight Vaudémont first sees her, he too knows nothing of her condition. He only gradually discovers the truth in the course of the central love scene, the passage that most fired Tchaikovsky's imagination, and with which he began the composition. Three times Vaudémont asks Iolanta for a red rose, and three times she offers him a white one.

There's a fairy-tale quality about *Iolanta*, but it's really more a fable about growing up. It has none of the cruelty found in so many real fairy tales, and there are no supernatural characters. Tchaikovsky admitted that what attracted him to the subject was 'its poetic quality, its originality and its profusion of lyrical moments'. Iolanta's dawning awareness of her blindness and the cure by which she regains her sight is an image of maturing and of sexual awakening which is treated with great sensitivity and tenderness. The prevailing mood of the music is that gentle melancholy which came so naturally to Tchaikovsky. He took

particular care over the instrumentation, and changes of situation, mood and character are often suggested not by events on stage but simply by delicate changes of orchestral colour.

As Iolanta recovers her sight at the end of the opera, she experiences wonder, but also a sense of fear; and the final ensemble has an appropriate touch of awe at the mystery of her cure – or rather, at the mystery of attraction and love.

For more fairy-tale music at the Proms, see pages 20–29

PROM
42
TCHAIKOVSKY
Iolanta; plus excerpts from The Nutcracker
Monday 15 August, 7.30pm

HANDEL: JULIUS CAESAR

Jonathan Keates celebrates Handel's supreme achievement in turning a dusty old chapter of ancient Roman history into a sensual operatic hymn to the enduring power of love

If we had to choose a 'signature' work among Handel's operas, it would surely be *Julius Caesar*. Premiered in London in 1724 (as *Giulio Cesare in Egitto*), it shows us the composer at the height of his powers, carefully refining and re-drafting his original ideas to suit the talents of a changing cast and working closely with the librettist Nicola Haym, among the most sympathetic of all his collaborators. Using a text originally prepared for the 17th-century Venetian composer Antonio Sartorio, Haym pared down the plot, added new scenes, but retained the basic amalgam of heroic adventure, amorous intrigue, tragic pathos and humorous irony.

The story is that of Caesar's pursuit of his defeated rival Pompey to Egypt in 48 BC. Following Pompey's murder at the hands of the evil pharaoh Ptolemy XII, Caesar joined forces with the king's sister Cleopatra, helping her gain the throne and winning her love in the process. Though the opera's libretto adds a subplot, involving a bid for vengeance against Ptolemy by Pompey's son Sextus, supported by his widowed mother Cornelia, Handel and Haym scarcely needed to tamper with such a robust historical narrative, its central figures already powerfully outlined.

Handel's Caesar is a fully-rounded hero, gallant, courageous, equal to the challenges of love and war, but a profound moralist when it suits him – as evidenced in 'Alma del gran Pompeo' ('Spirit of great Pompey'), his fine accompanied recitative in Act 1. The heroic dimension is broadened for us by the valiant boy warrior Sextus, to whose nobility the cynically villainous Ptolemy offers an obvious foil. Caught in the crossfire, as it were, is Cornelia, the archetypal Roman matriarch, whose successive arias show her learning to hope against hope as the opera asserts the triumph of love and peace over violence and cunning.

It is Cleopatra, however, who clearly fascinated Handel most of all. Her extraordinary mixture of fearlessness, emotional intensity, teasing eroticism and sheer boundless energy creates one of the most vividly defined female roles in the whole history of opera. Her triumph comes in the amazing Act 2 seduction scene, centred on the aria 'V'adoro, pupille' ('Eyes, I adore you'), where Handel, using a double orchestra with lavish instrumentation, designs a richly sensual framework around this 'serpent of old Nile', eternally feminine as goddess, temptress and muse. Her buoyant closing duet with Caesar ('Cara! Bella!') celebrates the potency of enduring love – something in which, if this brilliant score is anything to go by, Handel himself passionately believed (though whether he ever experienced it personally is another matter).

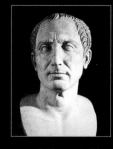

ABOVE
He came, he saw, he was conquered: marble bust of Julius Caesar (1st century BC)

BELOW
The Banquet of Cleopatra (c1744) by Tiepolo

PROM **52**	**HANDEL**
	Julius Caesar
	Tuesday 23 August, 6.00pm

LISZT: A FAUST SYMPHONY

Mike Ashman introduces Franz Liszt's masterly set of symphonic variations on a devilish theme

Dr Johann Faustus was a 16th-century magician, astrologer and charlatan who supposedly sold his soul to the Devil for a period of renewed youth. Spin-doctor versions of this legend became one of the seminal subjects for 19th-century Romantic painters, poets and composers, led by Goethe's great poetic drama *Faust*, which appeared in instalments in 1808 and 1832. Goethe's Faust was a frustrated philosopher, seeking worldly diversion from intellectual pursuits with the magical help of Mephistopheles – a devil, but one acting on God's command. Although he seduces and abandons the beautiful Gretchen and utters the forbidden words of longing that allow Mephistopheles to claim his soul, Faust is ultimately redeemed by his constant human quest for truth and knowledge.

Goethe's epic intellectualisation of the Faust legend was invoked in operas by Gounod and Boito, and in choral and orchestral scores by Schumann, Berlioz, Wagner, Mahler – and Franz Liszt, who, like Goethe, was for a time director of the Weimar court theatre. Introduced to Goethe's play by Berlioz in 1830, Liszt was at first wary of treating material by his stellar predecessor ('anything connected with Goethe is dangerous for me to handle') but he finally yielded to temptation as a result of conversations with the English novelist George Eliot and her partner George Henry Lewes, the Goethe biographer, while they were on a research trip to Weimar in the summer of 1854.

Working 'like a being possessed', Liszt wrote his score between August and October of that year. Dedicating it to Berlioz, he called it *A Faust Symphony in Three Character Sketches after Goethe*, assigning one movement each to Faust, Gretchen and Mephistopheles. Remarkable are the presence of a seeming 12-tone row in the slow introduction depicting Faust himself, the use of much-reduced orchestral forces in the Gretchen movement and the bold dramaturgical decision to give Mephistopheles no new music of his own, but brilliant, virtuosic distortions and reharmonisations of Faust's themes.

Prior to conducting the work's premiere – at the unveiling of a joint monument to Goethe and Schiller – in Weimar in September 1857, Liszt decided to append a vocal setting (for solo tenor and male-voice choir) of Goethe's concluding 'Chorus mysticus' in praise of the Eternal Feminine. But most conductors today tend to agree with the composer's future son-in-law, Wagner (who also famously borrowed from Liszt's score for Sieglinde's dream-sequence in Act 2 of *Die Walküre*), in preferring the original, purely orchestral ending, in which Faust's soul is taken up to Heaven to (in Wagner's words) 'a final, all-vanquishing reminiscence of Gretchen, full of tenderness and fragrance, and without any sense of exaggerated attention-grabbing'.

PROM
56
LISZT
A Faust Symphony
Friday 26 August, 7.30pm

VERDI: REQUIEM

Patrick O'Connor charts the unstoppable progress of a sacred masterpiece that the Church initially opposed and that some still consider the composer's 'finest opera'

Although his name is now synonymous with Italian opera, Verdi began and ended his career with sacred music. One of his earliest works, only recently rediscovered, is a solemn *Messa di Gloria*, composed when he was 20, and first performed in his home town of Busseto in 1833. His *Four Sacred Pieces* of 1898 were his final offering, composed just three years before his death.

The idea for the *Requiem* was first mooted in 1868, when Verdi had proposed a collaboration with several other leading Italian composers to honour the memory of Rossini, who had just died. This project never came to fruition, but five years later, on the death of the Italian novelist and playwright Alessandro Manzoni (1785–1873), Verdi decided to compose his own *Requiem* as a memorial to his friend, the man he called 'the purest, holiest, and highest of our glories'. And Verdi wanted the work's first performance to be given in a church, not a theatre.

Many eyebrows were raised at the time about Verdi's suitability for a sacred work. His anti-clerical stance was well known, and in making the *Requiem* a work (like Rossini's *Stabat mater*) for male and female voices, he was going against all the traditions of Italian church music. So there was some doubt as to whether the ecclesiastical authorities would permit the work's performance in church. Yet, on 22 May 1874, the premiere took place in the Chiesa San Marco in Milan. So successful was it that the work had to be repeated three days later at the La Scala opera house, and the following season Verdi took it on tour – to Paris, London and Vienna.

The London performances were at the Royal Albert Hall in May 1875, with the composer conducting, and while Verdi was disappointed by the size of the audience, the work was received enthusiastically by both critics and public. It was soon performed all over Europe, although Verdi was horrified when an unauthorised version appeared, arranged for brass band.

In the most hostile attack against the *Requiem*, written by Wagner's champion Hans von Bülow, the German conductor accused Verdi of despoiling Italian artistic taste, calling him 'the Attila of the larynx', and the *Requiem* 'a triumph of Latin barbarism'. Now, 130 years later, the *Requiem* has been accepted in church and opera house, in concert hall and recording studio. Verdi himself considered it one of his highest achievements: 'I feel as if I had become a serious man, and am no longer the public's clown.'

PROM
58
VERDI
Requiem
Sunday 28 August, 6.30pm

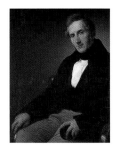

LEFT
Verdi conducting: portrait by T (pen-name of Theobald Chartran) from *Vanity Fair*, February 1879

ABOVE
Alessandro Manzoni, the Italian writer and patriot in whose memory Verdi wrote his *Requiem*: 1841 portrait by Francesco Hayez

BEETHOVEN: MISSA SOLEMNIS

Richard Wigmore describes how, in aiming to instil religious feeling in public and performers alike, Beethoven created a uniquely dramatic and highly personal setting of the Mass

'The day on which a High Mass composed by me will be performed during the ceremonies solemnised for your Imperial Highness will be the most glorious day of my life.' Beethoven had already embarked on a new Mass when he wrote these words to his benefactor and one-time pupil Archduke Rudolph in June 1819. But, true to form, he failed to finish it in time for Rudolph's enthronement as Archbishop of Olmütz (now Olomouc) the following March. The Mass, in fact, became his chief preoccupation for nearly four years. Every movement grew to an unforeseen scale as Beethoven sketched, chiselled and revised obsessively; and it was not until early in 1823 that he finally sent the Archduke his own dedicatory copy.

After finishing the Mass, Beethoven wrote to a friend: 'My chief aim was to awaken and permanently instil religious feelings not only into the singers but also into the listeners.' Like Schubert, Beethoven had no truck with the rituals and dogmas of orthodox Catholicism – it is telling, for instance, that he skips rapidly through the doctrinal clauses towards the end of the Credo. His faith was personal and heterodox, questioning rather than submissive and tinged with Enlightenment deism and Romantic pantheism. Beethoven quickly realised that the Mass's scale and complexity precluded normal liturgical use. Indeed, he stressed to publishers that it could be performed as an oratorio; and when the Kyrie, Credo and Agnus Dei were first heard in Vienna, in the famous concert of 7 May 1824 that included the premiere of the Ninth Symphony, they were billed, at the behest of the ecclesiastical censors, as 'Three Grand Hymns'.

Transcending the Classical Austrian liturgical tradition from which it grew, the *Missa solemnis* colours and dramatises the Mass text in an unprecedented way. With breathtaking compositional sophistication, Beethoven welds extreme, even violent, contrasts prompted by his individual response to the text into a series of mighty quasi-symphonic designs. Like Bach in his B minor Mass, he also created a work of encyclopedic scope. The mystical, modal 'Et

incarnatus est' recalls the 'Palestrina style' that Beethoven studied in depth before beginning the Mass. The gargantuan fugue that closes the Gloria seems to refract Beethoven's beloved Handel through his own craggy, harmonically visionary idiom.

Elsewhere there are moments of torrential, Dionysian energy (above all the opening of the Gloria), shades of the concerto (in the seraphic violin solo of the Benedictus), and even of the theatre, in the apocalyptic 'war' episodes that shatter the lilting serenity of the 'Dona nobis pacem'. The martial echoes still linger in the distant timpani rolls that intrude on the hushed final prayer for peace. And the abiding impression of this awesome, intensely personal work ('From the heart – may it return to the heart,' Beethoven wrote on the title page) is of faith won after a titanic struggle, yet to the end edged with disquiet, even doubt.

RIGHT
Beethoven holding the manuscript of his *Missa solemnis*: 1819 portrait by Joseph Stieler

PROM **62**	BEETHOVEN *Missa solemnis* Wednesday 31 August, 7.30pm

BRAHMS: A GERMAN REQUIEM

Calum MacDonald reveals the essential humanity at the heart of Brahms's vernacular Requiem – a joint memorial to the composer's mother and to his musical mentor

Brahms received a tremendous initial boost at the outset of his career when, in 1853, Robert Schumann publicly proclaimed the unknown 20-year-old from Hamburg as the one he had been waiting for: the 'hero' who would 'give ideal expression to the times'. Within three months Schumann was in an asylum, and Brahms was the object of extreme scepticism among many of his contemporaries. It was only towards the end of the 1860s that the musical world at large began to accept that he had, indeed, established himself as a contemporary master. That shift in perception was essentially achieved by the first performance in 1868 of *Ein deutsches Requiem* (A German Requiem), the largest work he ever wrote. At a stroke Brahms had added a new masterpiece to the grand tradition of sacred choral music, equally at home in cathedral or concert hall.

Schumann had foretold that 'when he waves his magic wand where the power of great orchestral and choral forces will aid him, then we shall be shown still more wonderful glimpses into the secrets of the spirit-world'. One of the things that makes Brahms's *German Requiem* such a personal glimpse into those secrets is its text. Rather than setting the traditional Latin text, Brahms made his own compilation of passages from Luther's German Bible, creating a similar structure to a Latin Requiem, but one with a highly individual slant. The use of German was to make the message more immediate and understandable to his contemporaries and compatriots, but the result is not a Requiem specifically for Germans. In fact Brahms once said his purpose would have been plainer if he'd called it a 'Human' rather than a 'German' Requiem, and he vigorously defended his chosen text, which controversially omitted all mention of the salvation in Christ that the Church authorities wished him to include.

A German Requiem demonstrates on the largest scale Brahms's mastery of form and his unique synthesis from the masters of the past whom, as a pioneer in reviving early music, he explored with an enthusiasm that puzzled many of his contemporaries. Not only Bach, but Gabrieli and especially Schütz, figure in the Requiem's ancestry. But it has remained one of the best-loved works in the repertoire, still speaking to us today, through Brahms's mixture of architectural grandeur and intimacy. The great fugues and apocalyptic visions coexist with movements that are sublimated waltzes and cradle-songs. Here he is clearly honouring people that he loved and had lost – above all Schumann, and his own mother, who died shortly before the work was begun and has her own special commemoration in the fifth movement, the last to be composed. In essence, Brahms's *German Requiem* addresses the living, not the dead, and seeks to assuage our sense of loss.

ABOVE (from top)
Brahms (1869 portrait by Josef Novak); Johanna, his mother (undated photograph); Robert Schumann, his mentor (1850 photograph)

LEFT
Martin Luther *(right)* and the Elector Johann Friedrich at the foot of the Cross: title-page from an edition of Luther's translation of the New Testament published in 1546, the year of his death

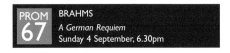

PROM
67
BRAHMS
A German Requiem
Sunday 4 September, 6.30pm

BBC SINGERS

2005 concerts include appearances in London, Paris, Belfast, Riga, Oxford, Kyoto, Aldeburgh, Tokyo, Portsmouth & Madrid

Chief Conductor
Stephen Cleobury

Principal Guest Conductor
Bob Chilcott

Associate Composer
Edward Cowie

Chief Repetiteur
Stephen Betteridge

"Warm, stylish singing and a good sense of drama ... a performance to remember."

The Classical Source, January 2005, MacMillan Weekend

For more information about forthcoming concerts, join the Friends of the BBC Singers
Tel 020 7765 1862   **Email** singers@bbc.co.uk   **www.bbc.co.uk/singers**

BBC RADIO 3
90-93 FM

Ellen Kent presents

Grigorovich's NUTCRACKER

'A spectacular production'
SUNDAY TIMES

The famous 1966 **Moscow production**. Directed by **Yuri Grigorovich**, Director of the **Bolshoi Ballet** for thirty years

A magical production boasting stunning scenery with flying boats, special effects and astonishing wizardry. With an impressive corps de ballet of over fifty dancers and a forty-piece orchestra.

CHILDREN COME FREE SUBJECT TO AVAILABILITY & RESTRICTIONS

NABUCCO

'A terrific production of Verdi's epic tale'
LIVERPOOL DAILY POST

Verdi's haunting and melodic chorus of the Hebrew slaves comes to life in a masterpiece of revenge, destruction and jealousy. A spectacular production with a 170 strong company.

Sung in Italian with English surtitles

ROYAL ALBERT HALL

Nabucco Friday 23 September 7·15pm
Nutcracker Monday 3 & Tuesday 4 October 7·15pm

Box Office 020 7589 8212
ticketmaster 0870 534 4444

All major credit cards and Switch accepted
Subject to booking/administration fee

The Sage Gateshead

an international home for music and musical discovery

"And the winner is . . . the Sage, Gateshead. For naive southerners venturing north, the discovery of the night was that Gateshead boasts a spectacular new hall on the banks of the Tyne."

The Guardian, 7 March 05

"Norman Foster's curvaceous new venue on the Tyne. A big, beautiful, democratic space, with exceptional acoustics designed to show off music of all kinds."

The Observer, 13 March 05

"The musicians loved the friendly acoustics and bold riverside presence of the Sage Gateshead."

Financial Times, 9 March 05

"The stunning new Sage Gateshead building, . . . promises to be a major musical resource centre in the North East. It is host to myriad concerts, and is committed to supporting schools in the area."

Times Education Supplement, 11 February 05

"Here they (Northern Sinfonia) showed off the hall's warm acoustic; the brass basking in a warm glow of hazy rapture, and the strings tautly responsive to Zehetmair's every gesture."

The Times, March 05

"The hall's tight, singing acoustic coped admirably, saturating the audience with reverberant sound of almost physical immediacy."

The Guardian, 24 January 05

"As a venue, the Sage is pure joy - exciting and inviting. The main hall and the recital hall, both acoustically hi-tech and adaptable, look wonderful, warm and intimate." *The Daily Telegraph, 27 November 04*

"The Sage Gateshead, a pioneering centre for musical performance on the south bank of the River Tyne . . . the most exciting new development on the British arts scene for many years."

The Independent, 6 December 04

"Even the words "spectacular concert hall" diminish the Sage. This vast Norman Foster creation on the Gateshead bank of the Tyne is far more than a concert hall. . . it will not only offer the most radical diet of music-making in Britain but also embody the regenerative aspirations of a community. In no other concert hall that I know is education given so central a place." *The Times, 15 November 04*

Tickets 0191 443 4661 • Enquiries 0191 443 4666
www.thesagegateshead.org

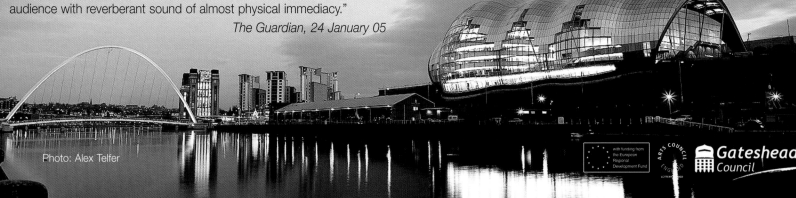

Photo: Alex Telfer

with funding from the European Regional Development Fund

ARTS COUNCIL ENGLAND

Gateshead Council

The BBC: bringing the Proms to you –
in concert, on radio, television and online

Advance Booking by post, fax and online *from Monday 16 May*
General Booking in person, by phone and online *from Monday 13 June*
Telephone: 020 7589 8212
For full booking information, see pages 133–148

bbc.co.uk/proms

CONCERT LISTINGS

BOOKING INFORMATION

For full booking information, see pages 133–148.

 Price Codes

Each concert falls into one of seven different price bands, colour-coded for easy reference. For details, see page 141.

SPECIAL OFFERS

 Weekend Promming Pass

Beat the weekend queues and save money too.

 Same Day Savers

Book for two concerts on the same day and save £4.00.

NEW: Groups & Under-16s

Group-booking and Under-16 discounts now apply to all concerts, except the Last Night

For full details of all special offers, see page 134.

NB: start-times vary across the season – check before you book.

Proms Extras: venue codes

RAH • Royal Albert Hall
WAF • West Arena Foyer, Royal Albert Hall
RGS • Royal Geographical Society
CH • Cadogan Hall

All concert details were correct at the time of going to press. The BBC reserves the right to alter artist or programme details as necessary

---

PROM 1

7.00pm – c9.30pm

Berlioz
Overture 'The Corsair'   8'

Mendelssohn
Violin Concerto in E minor   27'

Elgar
Overture 'Cockaigne'   13'

interval

Tippett
A Child of Our Time   66'

Janine Jansen *violin*
Indra Thomas *soprano*
Christine Rice *mezzo-soprano*
Ian Bostridge *tenor*
Sir Willard White *bass*

BBC Symphony Chorus
BBC Symphony Orchestra
Sir Roger Norrington *conductor*

Janine Jansen

A leading British conductor launches our Sea theme with Berlioz's exuberant overture; Elgar's colourful tour of Old London Town prefaces Tippett's powerful oratorio, which evocatively sets negro spirituals, to mark his centenary and the 60th anniversary of the end of the war. Former Radio 3 New Generation Artist Janine Jansen is the soloist in a first half which is televised for the first time on BBC1.

📖 *'The Sea', pages 4–13; 'Anniversary Composers', pages 36–38*
Broadcast on BBC1 (Part 1) and BBC2 (Part 2)

🔊 **5.30pm Pre-Prom Talk** (RGS)
Ian Kemp on Tippett's *A Child of Our Time*

PRICE B   WP

PROM 2

7.30pm – c10.00pm

Sullivan
The Yeomen of the Guard – overture 5'

Sullivan, arr. Mackerras
Pineapple Poll – suite   28'

interval

Gilbert & Sullivan
HMS Pinafore (with narration)   80'

Richard Suart *Sir Joseph Porter*
Neal Davies *Captain Corcoran*
Timothy Robinson *Ralph Rackstraw*
Sally Matthews *Josephine*
Felicity Palmer *Little Buttercup*
Peter Sidhom *Dick Deadeye*
Owen Gilhooly *Bill Bobstay*
Stephen Richardson *Bob Becket*

Maida Vale Singers
BBC Concert Orchestra
Sir Charles Mackerras *conductor*

Sir Charles Mackerras

Gilbert's satire on sea lords who know nothing about the sea, and Sullivan's memorable melodies combine in one of their most enduring comic creations, the story of 'the lass who loved a sailor'. The youthfully veteran Charles Mackerras conducts, also reviving his own ballet *Pineapple Poll*, which brilliantly re-orchestrates Sullivan's music, and is based on another sea satire by Gilbert.

📖 *'The Sea', pages 4–13; 'Season Highlights', page 67*
Recorded for later broadcast on BBC1

🔊 **6.00pm Pre-Prom Talk** (RAH)
Roderick Swanston on G&S

PRICE B   WP

PROM 3

6.30pm – c9.10pm

Purcell
The Fairy Queen
(concert performance)   148'

Rebecca Outram *soprano*
Mhairi Lawson *soprano*
Julia Gooding *soprano*
Susan Hemington Jones *soprano*
Daniel Auchincloss *tenor*
Charles Daniels *tenor*
Mark Le Brocq *tenor*
Peter Harvey *bass*
Andrew Foster-Williams *bass*

Gabrieli Consort & Players
Paul McCreesh *director*

Arthur Rackham: *The Meeting of Oberon and Titania*

A Midsummer Night's Dream in unusual guise: Purcell's lavish 'semi-opera' of 1692 interpolated masques and interludes into a bowdlerised version of Shakespeare, and conjured a magical world of fairies, pastoral comedy and the turning of the seasons in music of ethereal sensuality and vitality.

📖 *'Fairy Tales', pages 20–29; 'Season Highlights', page 68*
There will be one interval

🎞 **2.30pm Proms Films** (RGS)
A Midsummer Night's Dream

🔊 **5.00pm Pre-Prom Talk** (RAH)
Paul McCreesh and Nicholas Kenyon

PRICE A   WP

PROM 5

VAUGHAN WILLIAMS:
A London Symphony

The composer himself revised it. But once you've conducted the original version, says **Richard Hickox**, there's no going back

Ralph Vaughan Williams

Vaughan Williams followed his choral *Sea Symphony* (Prom 11) with a purely orchestral one – a symphonic portrait of London, premiered at the Queen's Hall in 1914. But he soon became disillusioned and, against the advice of colleagues, began to revise it. After it was published in the mid-1930s, this revised version became the only performing edition ... until, in 2001, the composer's widow Ursula sanctioned what was planned as a one-off recording of the original score, in which Richard Hickox conducted the London Symphony Orchestra. The response was so positive that two years later he was permitted to conduct its first public performance in modern times, and now he brings it to the Proms.

The symphony's 'epic Mahlerian grandeur' is restored, says Hickox. 'The second movement in particular gains enormously from the extra length, and it expands in the most logical way: in the revised version you can actually hear the joins. And there's a fascinating extra nine minutes at the end of the third movement, which looks forward to Holst's *The Planets*.'

Vaughan Williams said that he had excised some of the 'horrid modern music – awful stuff'. 'In fact,' says Hickox, 'he removed some of the most original music. I'm not sure I'd want to go back to the revised version now.'

BELOW
Claude Monet: Waterloo Bridge, 1902

Every Prom live on BBC Radio 3 and bbc.co.uk/proms
Advance Booking from 16 May • General Booking from 13 June: 020 7589 8212

86

MONDAY 18 JULY

PROM 4
5.00pm – c10.35pm

Wagner
Die Walküre (concert performance;
sung in German)   220'

Plácido Domingo Siegmund
Waltraud Meier Sieglinde
Eric Halfvarson Hunding
Bryn Terfel Wotan
Lisa Gasteen Brünnhilde
Rosalind Plowright Fricka
Geraldine McGreevy Gerhilde
Elaine McKrill Ortlinde
Claire Powell Waltraute
Rebecca de Pont Davies Schwertleite
Iréne Theorin Helmwige
Sarah Castle Siegrune
Clare Shearer Grimgerde
Elizabeth Sikora Rossweisse

**Orchestra of the
Royal Opera House
Antonio Pappano**
conductor

Plácido Domingo makes his long-awaited Proms debut in the cast of the Royal Opera's current production of Die Walküre, as the second instalment of our Proms *Ring* cycle, which began last year and will continue in 2006 and 2007.

Plácido Domingo

📖 'Season Highlights', page 69

There will be two intervals of 30 and 60 minutes
Broadcast on BBC4

🎵 **1.00pm Proms Chamber Music**
See pages 114–117

💬 **2nd interval: Proms Quiz** (WAF)
Hosted by Stephanie Hughes.
See page 127

PRICE
C

TUESDAY 19 JULY

PROM 5
7.00pm – c9.15pm

Michael Berkeley
Concerto for Orchestra   c25'
BBC commission: world premiere

Britten
Quatre chansons françaises   13'

interval

Vaughan Williams
A London Symphony
(original version)   61'

Susan Gritton soprano

**BBC National Orchestra of Wales
Richard Hickox** conductor

Recently awarded the Ralph Vaughan Williams Society's first Medal of Honour, Richard Hickox presents the original version of the composer's symphonic tribute to London (see left), alongside a new work by Michael Berkeley, the BBC NOW's Composer in Association, and an early song-cycle by his godfather, Benjamin Britten.

Richard Hickox

📖 'New Music', pages 50–57

Broadcast on BBC4

🔊 **5.30pm Pre-Prom Talk** (RGS)
Michael Berkeley discusses his new work with Richard Hickox and Tommy Pearson

PRICE
A

Michael Berkeley's Concerto for Orchestra (Kunsthalle (Monet); Lebrecht Music & Arts (Vaughan Williams); Clive Barda (Bryn Terfel as Wotan); Sheila Rock (Domingo); Greg Barrett (Hickox)

PROM 6

7.00pm – c9.10pm

Thea Musgrave
Turbulent Landscapes   30'
London premiere

Rakhmaninov
Piano Concerto No. 1
in F sharp minor   27'

interval

Nielsen
Symphony No. 4, 'The Inextinguishable'   36'

Stephen Hough *piano*

BBC Symphony Orchestra
Osmo Vänskä *conductor*

Following his BBC SO Proms debut last year, Osmo Vänskä returns with Nielsen's symphonic celebration of the 'Elemental Will of Life' (with its riotous exchange for two sets of timpani), Rakhmaninov's showcase concerto (*see right*) and Thea Musgrave's new set of Turneresque seascapes (which the BBC SO introduced to the UK last year).

Stephen Hough

📖 'The Sea', pages 4–13
Broadcast on BBC4

▶ **5.15pm Composer Portrait**
(RAH)
Thea Musgrave. *See page 125*

PROM 7

10.15pm – c11.40pm

Haydn
Motet 'Insanae et vanae curae'   8'

Symphony No. 90 in C major   24'

Missa in angustiis ('Nelson' Mass)   39'

Luba Orgonášová *soprano*
Wilke te Brummelstroete
mezzo-soprano
Robert Murray *tenor*
Alastair Miles *bass*

Monteverdi Choir
English Baroque Soloists
Sir John Eliot Gardiner *conductor*

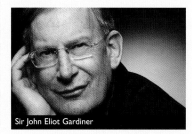
Sir John Eliot Gardiner

The rousing 'Nelson' Mass marks the centenary of the Battle of Trafalgar, a key-point in the season's Sea theme, in the summer's first Late Night Prom, under period-performance guru Sir John Eliot Gardiner. An unjustly neglected Haydn motet promoting heavenly thoughts precedes the composer's 90th Symphony.

📖 'The Sea', pages 4–13
There will be no interval

PROM 6

RAKHMANINOV: Piano Concerto No. 1

Fresh from recording all four Rakhmaninov piano concertos live in Dallas, Stephen Hough brings his interpretation of the First (or should that be Fourth?) to this year's Proms

Unlikely as it may sound, Stephen Hough first learnt Rakhmaninov's Piano Concerto No. 1 as a result of a promise made to the composer by one Gitta Gradova (1904–85). A child prodigy, Gradova gave up her career in 1942 to be a mother, but promised Rakhmaninov she would one day learn his First Concerto. In her 80th year, more than 40

Rakhmaninov shakes hands with Henry Wood in 1938

years after the composer's death, a performance was finally arranged with the Chicago Symphony under James Levine. Tragically, she died three months before the concert, and it was Hough who was asked to take her place.

'It's false to think of the First Concerto as Rakhmaninov's "Op. 1",' says Hough, referring to Rakhmaninov's thorough revision of the work in 1917, more than 25 years after its premiere. 'By the time he revised the piece he had already written his Second and Third Concertos. In a way, this is really the Fourth Concerto, and the Fourth is actually the Fifth.'

Many of the Rakhmaninov hallmarks are there: the nostalgic vein ('The second movement has one of those tunes that Cole Porter would have been proud of'), the sparkling virtuosity and the dark orchestral colouring – as Hough points out, the composer 'wasn't one for pastel shades'.

Hough's live set of all four Rakhmaninov concertos was released last year to wide acclaim – perhaps unsurprisingly, given that he grew up with the composer's own recordings, though he's quick to point out that he follows them to the spirit rather than to the letter. He's keen too to rebut the charge that Rakhmaninov's music is unadventurous. 'The view that he was a sentimental, third-rate composer belongs to the period of flared trousers and platform shoes. No serious musicologist today would subscribe to it. We're realising more and more what an original composer Rakhmaninov was.'

Every Prom live on BBC Radio 3 and bbc.co.uk/proms
Advance Booking from 16 May • General Booking from 13 June: 020 7589 8212

87

PROM 8

7.30pm – c9.45pm

PROM 9

7.30pm – c9.40pm

PROM 10

11.00am – c1.00pm

PROM 11

7.30pm – c9.45pm

Stravinsky
The Nightingale *(concert performance; sung in Russian)*　　　50'

interval

James MacMillan
A Scotch Bestiary*　　　33'
BBC co-commission with Los Angeles Philharmonic: London premiere

Ravel
La valse　　　12'

Wayne Marshall *organ**
Olga Trifonova *Nightingale*
Ailish Tynan *Cook*
Evgeny Akimov *Fisherman*
Sergei Leiferkus *Emperor*
Darren Jeffery *Chamberlain*
Daniel Borowski *Bonze*
Irina Tchistyakova *Death*

BBC Singers
BBC Philharmonic
Gianandrea Noseda *conductor*
James MacMillan *conductor**

Stravinsky's exotic re-imagining of a Chinese fairy tale by Hans Christian Andersen prefaces James MacMillan's new 'fantasy menagerie' and Ravel's dark dissection of the Viennese waltz.

Wayne Marshall

📖 *'Fairy Tales', pages 20–29; 'New Music', pages 50–57*

Broadcast on BBC4

💬 **c9.50pm Proms Question Time** (WAF) See page 125

Mozart
Violin Concerto No. 3 in G major, K216　　　24'

interval

Mahler
Symphony No. 5 in C sharp minor　　　73'

Christian Tetzlaff *violin*

Philharmonia Orchestra
Christoph von Dohnányi *conductor*

Christoph von Dohnányi

One of today's greatest interpreters of the Austro-German Romantic repertory, Christoph von Dohnányi conducts Mahler's turbulent Fifth Symphony, with its heart-wrenching Adagietto – a love-gift from the composer to his wife. Before the interval, we welcome back Christian Tetzlaff for Mozart's folk-influenced Violin Concerto No. 3.

Broadcast on BBC4

BLUE PETER PROM
– Out of this World

Konnie Huq *presenter*
Zoe Salmon *presenter*
Gethin Jones *presenter*

New London Children's Choir
BBC Philharmonic
Jason Lai *conductor*

Once upon a time there was a *Blue Peter* presenter called Konnie who loved performing at the Proms so much that this year she is bringing her two newest *Blue Peter* friends to share in an action-packed voyage across the high seas of music by Britten and Debussy, into the fairy-tale worlds of *Cinderella, Beauty and the Beast*, and Tchaikovsky's Nutcracker and Sugar Plum Fairy. On the way, amid lots of fun and surprises, they meet the magician of Dukas's *Sorcerer's Apprentice*, whose themes were immortalised by Mickey Mouse in Walt Disney's film *Fantasia*. And finally, with massed children's choirs, they invite the whole audience to join in with favourite tunes from the traditional Last Night festivities, and to live happily ever after in the huge round concert hall in Kensington – right opposite the park where you can find the statue of the most famous 'boy who never grew up' (even though he is now 100 years old!): Peter Pan!

There will be one interval
Recorded for later broadcast on CBBC

Mendelssohn
Overture 'The Hebrides' ('Fingal's Cave')　　　10'

Bruch
Violin Concerto No. 1 in G minor　　　25'

interval

Vaughan Williams
A Sea Symphony　　　65'

Leila Josefowicz *violin*
Janice Watson *soprano*
Dwayne Croft *baritone*

Royal Liverpool Philharmonic Choir
Chester Festival Chorus
Royal Liverpool Philharmonic Orchestra
Gerard Schwarz *conductor*

Mendelssohn's bubbling postcard from the Hebrides and Vaughan Williams's epic setting of sea poems by Walt Whitman frame the ever-popular Violin Concerto by Max Bruch (a former Principal Conductor of the RLPO), in which we welcome back the soloist of the 2003 Last Night.

Leila Josefowicz

📖 *'The Sea', pages 4–13*

Broadcast on BBC4

PRICE A　　PRICE A 　　PRICE G 　　PRICE A

PROM 12

3.30pm – c5.30pm

BLUE PETER PROM
– Out of this World

Konnie Huq *presenter*
Zoe Salmon *presenter*
Gethin Jones *presenter*

New London Children's Choir
BBC Philharmonic
Jason Lai *conductor*

See Prom 10
for details.

Konnie Huq

Zoe Salmon

Gethin Jones

There will be one interval

Recorded for later broadcast on CBBC

PROM 13

7.30pm – c9.40pm

Elgar
The Dream of Gerontius   97'

Alice Coote *mezzo-soprano*
Paul Groves *tenor*
Matthew Best *bass*

Hallé Youth Choir
Hallé Choir
London Philharmonic Choir
Hallé
Mark Elder *conductor*

Mark Elder (see right), one of our most probing interpreters of Elgar, continues his flourishing partnership with the Hallé, with whom he has already recorded many of the composer's works. Elgar's visionary setting of Cardinal Newman's poem follows Gerontius's uncertain journey from his deathbed into the beyond. For Elgar it was an affirmation of his Catholic faith, written from his 'insidest inside', and a peak in his handling of choral-orchestral forces. 'This is the best of me …' he wrote on the score; 'this, if anything of mine, is worth your memory.'

Mark Elder

There will be one interval

Broadcast on BBC4

PROM 13

ELGAR: The Dream of Gerontius

Hallé music director Mark Elder recalls his conversion to Elgar's great vision of one man's spiritual journey to meet his maker

'My first encounter with Elgar's *The Dream of Gerontius* was in the 1960s, when I was obliged to study it, very inadequately, as an A-level set work. The Victorian prose of Cardinal Newman's text was very difficult for me at that stage, as was the whole world of "smells and bells". But from the moment I heard the music I felt it was a very special work.

In the last 15 years Elgar's music has come to mean more and more to me, and I think his unusual balance of outward confidence but inner nervousness has produced a number of very great masterworks. At the time, of course, Elgar was only just beginning to find his feet. The *Enigma Variations* was really the thing that made an impact on everybody. But nothing that would have prepared them for the enormous step forward that Elgar took with *Gerontius*.

Once the extraordinary prelude is behind us, there are still many wonderful moments to come: Gerontius's death, so delicately and exquisitely timed by Elgar and the immediate contrast with the arrival of the Priest intoning "Proficiscere, anima Christiana" ("Go forth upon thy journey, Christian soul"); the completely unexpected, otherworldly music that begins Part 2, portraying in sound the idea of the soul having passed over; the first meeting with the Angel; the enormous impact that the double chorus "Praise to the Holiest in the height" can make; and the Angel's eventual farewell in the final moments of the work.

Elgar was largely self-taught: his understanding of the orchestra came from listening whenever he could – as a young boy in Worcestershire, and then increasingly in London – like a magpie I always think, observing rehearsals and concerts. This gave him his technique, and *Gerontius* is the first very large-scale work in which Elgar was able to exhibit it.'

RIGHT Elgar memorial window in Worcester Cathedral

Every Prom live on BBC Radio 3 and bbc.co.uk/proms
Advance Booking from 16 May • General Booking from 13 June: 020 7589 8212

PROM 14

7.00pm – c9.05pm

Tippett
The Vision of St Augustine   38'

interval

Shostakovich
Symphony No. 10 in E minor   55'

Elizabeth Atherton *soprano*
Roderick Williams *baritone*

BBC Symphony Chorus
BBC National Orchestra of Wales
Richard Hickox *conductor*

Michael Tippett

We continue our Tippett centenary celebrations with the composer's rarely-performed cantata exploring the 4th-century saint's transcendent vision of eternity. Written in the wake of Stalin's death, Shostakovich's Tenth Symphony revels in Russia's new-found freedom of expression.

📖 *'Anniversary Composers', pages 36–38*
Broadcast on BBC4

───────────────

🎵 **1.00pm Proms Chamber Music**
See pages 114–117
🎤 **5.30pm Pre-Prom Talk (RAH)**
John Butt on Tippett's *Vision*

PROM 15

7.30pm – c9.50pm

Lyadov
Baba-Yaga; The Enchanted Lake;
Kikimora   20'

Oliver Knussen
Whitman Settings   10'

Detlev Glanert
Theatrum bestiarum   c20'
BBC commission: world premiere

interval

Stravinsky
The Fairy's Kiss   43'

Claire Booth *soprano*

BBC Symphony Orchestra
Oliver Knussen *conductor*

Oliver Knussen premieres a new BBC commission from Detlev Glanert, whose Third Symphony made such an impression at the Proms in 1996, alongside his own settings of four Walt Whitman poems. Stravinsky's fairy-tale ballet on themes from Tchaikovsky and Hans Christian Andersen is contrasted with Lyadov's trilogy of tone-poems on more traditional Russian folk tales.

📖 *'Fairy Tales', pages 20–29;*
'New Music' pages 50–57

Broadcast on BBC4

───────────────

🎤 **5.30pm Composer Portrait (RAH)**
Detlev Glanert. See page 125

PROM 16

7.00pm – c9.05pm

Ravel
Mother Goose – suite   18'

Henri Dutilleux
Correspondances   20'
London premiere

interval

Stravinsky
Scherzo fantastique   16'

Musorgsky, orch. Ravel
Pictures at an Exhibition   32'

Barbara Hannigan *soprano*

**City of Birmingham
Symphony Orchestra**
Sakari Oramo *conductor*

Ravel's storybook suite and his colourful transformation of Musorgsky's black-and-white *Pictures* frame Stravinsky's 'fantastical scherzo' and a highly-praised new French

Barbara Hannigan

song-cycle from France's senior composer – introduced to the UK by the CBSO earlier this year – setting epistolary texts by Solzhenitsyn, Rilke, Van Gogh and Prithwindra Mukherjee.

📖 *'Fairy Tales', pages 20–29;*
'New Music' pages 50–57

Broadcast on BBC4

PROM 17

10.00pm – c11.20pm

Beethoven
The Creatures of Prometheus –
overture   6'

Tippett
Divertimento on Sellinger's Round   18'

Mozart
Concert arias: 'Bella mia fiamma';
'Chi sà, chi sà, qual sia'   13'

Beethoven
Symphony No. 8 in F major   27'

Kate Royal *soprano*

Manchester Camerata
Douglas Boyd *conductor*

The Manchester Camerata makes its Proms debut, last year's Kathleen Ferrier Award winner sings Mozart arias, Proms centenary composer Michael Tippett evokes British music across the centuries, and Beethoven's sparkling Eighth Symphony contrasts with his ballet overture in praise of the mythical Greek creator of mankind.

Kate Royal

📖 *'Anniversary Composers', pages 36–38*
There will be no interval

PRICE **A**   PRICE **A**   PRICE **A**   PRICE **D**

PROM 18
7.30pm – c9.45pm

John Adams
The Chairman Dances _13'_

John Corigliano
Violin Concerto, 'The Red Violin' _38'_
UK premiere

interval

Prokofiev
Romeo and Juliet – excerpts _45'_

Joshua Bell _violin_

**Bournemouth Symphony
Orchestra**
Marin Alsop _conductor_

Joshua Bell returns to the Proms with Corigliano's new concerto (see right). Adams's _The Chairman Dances_ revisits a moment in his hugely successful 'docu-opera' _Nixon in China_, while Prokofiev's glorious ballet music revisits one of the most enduring romances of all time (see also Prom 23).

Joshua Bell

📖 _'New Music', pages 50–57_
Broadcast on BBC4

♪ **4.00pm Young Composers Concert (CH)** See page 125

🔊 **6.00pm Pre-Prom Talk (RAH)**
John Corigliano and Marin Alsop

PROM 19
7.30pm – c9.45pm

Tchaikovsky
The Snow Maiden – Introduction; Melodrama; Dance of the Tumblers _15'_

Shostakovich
Violin Concerto No. 1 in A minor _37'_

interval

Prokofiev
Symphony No. 5 in B flat minor _46'_

Sergey Khachatryan _violin_

BBC Philharmonic
Vassily Sinaisky _conductor_

Tchaikovsky's music for a fairy-tale play by Ostrovsky opens an all-Russian Prom from the BBC Philharmonic under its Russian-born Principal Guest Conductor. While Prokofiev's wartime 'symphony of the greatness of the human spirit' patriotically embraced the prevailing Socialist Realist ideals, Shostakovich's First Violin Concerto – here played by 20-year-old Armenian virtuoso Sergey Khachatryan – had to be hidden away until after Stalin's death.

Sergey Khachatryan

📖 _'Fairy Tales', pages 20–29_
Broadcast on BBC4

PROM 18

CORIGLIANO: 'The Red Violin' Concerto

You've seen the film, now hear the concerto – brought to the Proms for its UK premiere by Joshua Bell

François Girard's 1999 film _The Red Violin_ traces the turbulent journey of a unique instrument across three centuries and three continents. While the film itself stars Samuel L. Jackson, the star of John Corigliano's Oscar-winning soundtrack was none other than American violinist Joshua Bell, who was, as he recalls, approached by Girard (who also made _Thirty-Two Short Films about Glenn Gould_) after a Wigmore Hall concert in London and asked to be 'the "voice" of the violin'.

'While we were working on the film,' Bell explains, 'I took the opportunity to commission Corigliano to write some more music based on musical ideas from it.' The result was a 17-minute _Chaconne_, which Bell included on the soundtrack recording and toured across the USA. Like the violin of Girard's film, Corigliano's music has re-emerged in further unexpected guises, including a set of _Caprices_ and a Suite for violin and orchestra, and in 2003 the composer added three further movements to the _Chaconne_ to form a _Red Violin_ Concerto.

Bell is proud to have been associated with the work from the start: 'Because I've been able to make certain suggestions – whether I can play an octave higher here, or add some double-stopping there – I feel I've helped give birth to it. But basically the approach is the same as for the great Romantic concertos: you have to get inside the piece and figure out what story you're telling.'

As it happens, Bell's 'Gibson' Stradivari has its own story to tell – having been twice stolen from the Polish violinist Bronislaw Huberman before falling into Bell's hands. But that's perhaps the subject for another film.

'The Red Violin' will be shown on Sunday 31 July: for details, see page 126.

Every Prom live on BBC Radio 3 and bbc.co.uk/proms
Advance Booking from 16 May • General Booking from 13 June: 020 7589 8212

91

PROM 20
2.30pm – c4.00pm

PROM 21
7.00pm – c9.10pm

PROM 22
10.00pm – c11.30pm

PROM 23
6.30pm – c8.15pm

Young players and professionals join together for the first time at the Proms to create a spectacular three-part day of music-making, with debate on the new Music Manifesto. Alongside a new violin concerto written for the brilliant Viktoria Mullova, talented young players from workshops around the UK join the BBC Symphony Orchestra in a huge performance of *The Pines of Rome*, as well as a new work they have created themselves. In a family matinee, the Northern Sinfonia brings works for one, two, four and more violins, while the late-night concert will make the Royal Albert Hall resound with Scottish fiddles and exotic gypsy violins.

Bach
Partita No. 3 in E major – excerpts   6'

Hartmann
Sonata No. 2, for solo violin – excerpts 5'

Bartók
Duos, for two violins – selection   9'

Vivaldi
Concerto in B minor for four violins,
Op. 3 No. 10, RV 580   10'

Grieg
Holberg Suite   20'

Britten
Simple Symphony   17'

Jennifer Pike *violin*
Viktoria Mullova *violin*
Bradley Creswick *violin*
Kyra Humphreys *violin*
Peter Campbell-Kelly *violin*

Northern Sinfonia
Thomas Zehetmair *violin/conductor*

There will be no interval

♪ **5.00pm 'Tell Tchaikovsky
the news ...'** (RGS)
Presented by the Music Manifesto
(see *opposite*)
Howard Goodall and young musicians
demonstrate new ways of music-making,
and debate the future of music education
in a creative forum open to all.

Bernstein
Candide – overture   5'

Fraser Trainer
for the living (Violin Concerto)   c25'
BBC commission: world premiere

interval

Britten
The Young Person's Guide
to the Orchestra   18'

Invisible Lines   c10'
*new work created by Between The Notes,
musicians from the BBC SO and young
musicians from Berkshire, Cheltenham,
Gateshead and Southampton*

Respighi
The Pines of Rome   23'

Viktoria Mullova *violin*

Musicians from:
**Berkshire Young Musicians
Trust Ensemble
Cheltenham Music Festival
Youth Ensemble
Southampton Youth Orchestra
The Sage Gateshead
Weekend School**

**Between The Notes
BBC Symphony Orchestra
Martyn Brabbins** *conductor*

📖 *'New Music', pages 50–57*
Broadcast on BBC4

Blazin' Fiddles
Roby Lakatos Ensemble

Blazin' Fiddles is a virtuoso ensemble presenting a celebration of the fiddle traditions of Scotland. There is a rare opportunity to hear pieces featuring the regional style of each individual fiddler, creating the distinctive flavours of highland and islands fiddle music; then the contrasted styles and different players come together in a riot of colourful combinations, as fiddles and bows blaze away. Blazin' Fiddles has been called 'one of the hottest tickets in the traditional music world'.

Roby Lakatos and his gypsy band return to the Proms following their hugely popular 2001 concert to create their own exotic brand of gypsy magic: Lakatos is one of the world's greatest violin virtuosos in any style (as his appearances alongside such players as Maxim Vengerov and Didier Lockwood have demonstrated), and his playing shows the full range and intense passion of the gypsy tradition.

Roby Lakatos

There will be no interval

Berlioz
Romeo and Juliet (*sung in French*)   95'

Katarina Karnéus *mezzo-soprano*
Jean-Paul Fouchécourt *tenor*
John Relyea *bass*

**London Symphony Chorus
BBC Scottish Symphony Orchestra
Ilan Volkov** *conductor*

It was the spontaneous gift of 20,000 francs from the celebrated violinist Paganini that bought Berlioz the time to compose his 'dramatic symphony' based on Shakespeare's play. With an

Ilan Volkov

introduction that vividly depicts the warring families of the Capulets and Montagues, a deftly painted orchestral Love Scene and a waspish Queen Mab Scherzo – linking up with this year's Proms fairy-tale theme – it was a labour of love in honour of the English bard who, Berlioz wrote, 'struck me down with a thunderbolt ... opened to me the highest heaven of art'.

📖 *'Season Highlights', page 70*
There will be no interval
Broadcast live on BBC4

🎞 **2.30pm Proms Films** (RGS)
The Red Violin

PRICE

PRICE

PRICE

PRICE

PROM 24

7.30pm – c9.40pm

Sibelius
Symphony No. 3 in C major   30'

Hans Abrahamsen
Four Pieces for Orchestra   16'
UK premiere

interval

Brahms
Piano Concerto No. 2 in B flat major   50'

Nelson Freire piano

BBC Scottish Symphony Orchestra
Ilan Volkov conductor

In their second Prom this season, Ilan Volkov
and the BBC Scottish Symphony perform
Sibelius's Third Symphony – one of the first
works composed at the composer's lakeside
refuge north of Helsinki – before the UK
premiere of Hans Abrahamsen's *Four Pieces
for Orchestra*. Brilliant Argentine pianist
Nelson Freire joins them in Brahms's stirring
Second Piano Concerto.

📖 'New Music', pages 50–57

🎵 **I.00pm Proms Chamber Music**
See pages 114–117

💬 **5.30pm Composer Portrait**
(RAH)
Hans Abrahamsen. See page 125

PRICE A

PROMS 20–22
VIOLINS!! VIOLINS!! VIOLINS!!

The violin has had surely the most
varied and spectacular life of any
orchestral instrument, from its origins
in lively, popular dance-music to its
sudden emergence in the 17th century
as a sophisticated vehicle for
virtuosity. From Bach's great sonatas
and partitas to the flashy writing of
Paganini, through the great 20th-
century concertos of Shostakovich,
Prokofiev and Bartók, the violin has
responded to every twist and turn of
musical history. Its folk heritage
remains undimmed in fiddle bands
and gypsy groups around Europe, and
it has been reinvented in electric guise
for a new generation.

Following in the tradition of
large-scale Proms events such as
Choral Day and Millennium Youth
Day, this year's violin day begins with
the notes of a single unaccompanied
violin and works through the sounds
of a massive full orchestra to the
exuberance of folk and gypsy fiddles;
it will show something of the violin's
wide appeal as a solo instrument and
its function as a linchpin of the
modern orchestra.

Jennifer Pike, BBC Young
Musician of the Year 2002, launches
the day, leading virtuosos Thomas
Zehetmair and Viktoria Mullova pick
up the bow in Bartók duos, and the
crack players of the Northern Sinfonia
– all three concerts draw on the skills
of ensembles linked to the successful
new Sage Gateshead music centre –
play favourite pieces for strings. In the
main evening concert, Mullova is
heard again in a newly commissioned
concerto by the young British
composer Fraser Trainer.

Bringing together especially
talented young orchestral players with
the professionals of the BBC
Symphony Orchestra is a new Proms
initiative developed in conjunction
with the ensemble Between The Notes.
More than an 'education event', it aims
to create music-making of the highest
quality in a special family concert
including Britten's ever-fresh *Young
Person's Guide*. In recent months
Between The Notes, with members of
the BBC SO, has visited four UK
centres and worked with young
players: they have created a work of
their own which will be performed in
this concert. Then young and not-so-
young will join in a large-scale account
of Respighi's glorious *Pines of Rome*.

Viktoria Mullova

Thomas Zehetmair

Finally, the roots of the violin in
popular culture are celebrated with a
wonderful folk-fiddling ensemble from
Scotland and a gypsy violin band from
Europe. Viva violins!

The Music Manifesto

The Music Manifesto, launched in 2004,
aims to:
- provide every young person with
  access to a range of musical experiences
- provide opportunities for young people
  to deepen their musical interests
- identify and nurture our most
  talented musicians
- develop a world-class workforce for
  music education
- improve support structures for young
  people's music-making

Over 170 organisations and individuals
involved in music education have signed up
to the Manifesto, including the BBC.
Celebrate the Music Manifesto at BBC
Proms 2005. www.musicmanifesto.co.uk

Blazin' Fiddles

Every Prom live on BBC Radio 3 and bbc.co.uk/proms
Advance Booking from 16 May • General Booking from 13 June: 020 7589 8212

93

PROM 26

BERIO: Coro

Two years after Luciano Berio's death, we mark what would have been the Italian composer's 80th birthday year with a rare performance of his choral protest song

Composed in the mid-1970s, Luciano Berio's *Coro* marries together two very different forms of expression: folk-texts – from places as far-flung as North and South America, Polynesia, Africa, Croatia and Persia – and lines from the exiled Chilean poet Pablo Neruda's three-volume collection *Residencia en la tierra*. Just as the work's texts are intermingled, so are the choral-orchestral forces: each of the 40 singers is paired on stage with one of the 40 instrumentalists, allowing not only for large, carefully-integrated, choral-orchestral outbursts for the Neruda texts, but also a focus on individual pairings.

Diego Masson, who conducts the late-night performance with the London Sinfonietta and London Sinfonietta Voices, and who worked regularly with Berio, considers the work 'a real masterpiece'. It was, he points out, the continuation of a long line of folk-song-related pieces by Berio, which began with his *Folk Songs* of 1964 and ended with his *Voci* for viola and orchestra, written 20 years later. 'The interesting thing,' Masson adds, 'is that Berio allocated the folk-song texts, which have no author, to individual voices. It's a piece, in a way, which reflects the singing of the world and speaks of nations. The folk-song texts he uses are about death, love, work and nature – about life – and they are contrasted with Neruda's poems, also on the same subjects, but in a tragic way.' In fact, it is Neruda's lines *'venid a ver la sangre por las calles'* ('come and see the blood in the streets') – written as a savage indictment of Fascist atrocities in the Spanish Civil War, but lent a more universal import in Berio's setting – that provide the work's recurring refrain.

BELOW Pablo Picasso: *Guernica*, 1937

Every Prom live on BBC Radio 3 and bbc.co.uk/proms
Advance Booking from 16 May • General Booking from 13 June: 020 7589 8212

94

PROM 25
7.00pm – c9.00pm

Rameau
Les Paladins – suite   25'

Handel
Semele – 'Where'er you walk'; Jephtha – 'Waft her, angels'; 'His mighty arm'   15'

interval

Rameau
Dardanus – Chaconne; Prelude and Air 'Lieux funestes'; Recitative and Ariette 'Où suis-je? ... Hâtons-nous; courons à la gloire'   14'

Handel
Water Music – Suite in F major   25'

John Mark Ainsley *tenor*

**Philharmonia Baroque Orchestra
Nicholas McGegan** *conductor*

John Mark Ainsley

This year's Proms sea theme takes a trip down the River Thames with the buoyant suite that Handel wrote for a royal barge party. Nicholas McGegan brings his San Francisco-based period band to the UK for the first time, in a programme including excerpts from early and late operas by Rameau and arias from two great Handel oratorios.

🗨 **5.30pm Pre-Prom Event** (RGS)
Introduction to Baroque instruments

PROM 26
10.00pm – c11.35pm

Weill
Kleine Dreigroschenmusik   22'

Berio
Coro   53'

**London Sinfonietta Voices
London Sinfonietta
Diego Masson** *conductor*

Anniversary composer Luciano Berio's choral masterpiece (see *left*) is here paired with the signature work of an earlier composer whose music he loved and also arranged: Kurt Weill, who first shot to fame with his 1928 cabaret-style collaboration with Bertolt Brecht on *The Threepenny Opera*.

BELOW *The Threepenny Opera*: 1931 song-album cover

Berio

There will be no interval

PROM 27
7.30pm – c10.15pm

PROM 28
7.00pm – c8.50pm

PROM 29
10.00pm – c11.30pm

PROM 30
7.30pm – c9.35pm

Param Vir
Horse Tooth White Rock*   24'

Ravi Shankar
Sitar Concerto No. 1*   c40'

interval

Sandhya (evening) ragas   c60'

Ravi Shankar sitar
Anoushka Shankar sitar
with **Tanmoy Bose** tabla

BBC Symphony Orchestra*
Jurjen Hempel conductor*

Ravi Shankar, who this year celebrates his 85th birthday, premiered his Sitar Concerto No. 1 in London; tonight it is performed by his daughter and protégée Anoushka. Delhi-born Param Vir's 1994 BBC Philharmonic commission is named after the mountain at which an 11th-century Tibetan saint attained enlightenment. The concert closes with a sequence of evening ragas.

Ravi and Anoushka Shankar

🔊 **5.45pm Pre-Prom Event** (RAH)
Introduction to Indian Classical Music.

Mats Bäcker (Otter)

Dukas
La Péri   21'

Huw Watkins
Double Concerto for viola and cello c20'
world premiere

interval

Stravinsky
Petrushka (1947 version)   34'

Philip Dukes viola
Josephine Knight cello

BBC National Orchestra of Wales
Jac van Steen conductor

BBC NOW's newly-appointed Principal Guest Conductor unveils a new double concerto by one of Britain's brightest young composers, plus two ballet scores written for Diaghilev: Dukas's fairy-tale Persian *pas de deux*, and Stravinsky's tragic puppet love-triangle.

Vaslav Nijinsky as
Petrushka, 1911

📖 *'Fairy Tales', pages 20–29;
'New Music', pages 50–57*

 **5.30pm Pre-Prom Talk** (RGS)
Huw Watkins, Philip Dukes and Josephine Knight with Anthony Burton

---

Telemann
Suite in C major, 'Hamburger Ebb'
und Flut'   22'

Handel
Duets   c20'

Bach
Suite No. 4 in D major, BWV 1069   21'

Maria Cristina Kiehr soprano
Daniel Taylor counter-tenor

Akademie für Alte Musik Berlin

Founded in the former East Germany, the conductorless period-instrument Akademie für Alte Musik makes its Proms debut in music by Bach and Handel, plus a tidal suite by their Hamburg-based contemporary, Telemann.

📖 *'The Sea', pages 4–13*
There will be no interval

Tchaikovsky
Francesca da Rimini   24'

Mahler
Rückert-Lieder   22'

interval

Tubin
Toccata   6'

Sibelius
Symphony No. 5 in E flat major   30'

Anne Sofie von Otter mezzo-soprano

Gothenburg Symphony Orchestra
Neeme Järvi conductor

In his final tour after 22 years as Principal Conductor of this Swedish orchestra, Neeme Järvi marks the centenary of fellow Estonian Eduard Tubin in a concert that also includes Tchaikovsky's dramatic fantasy on a love-story from Dante, Mahler's five settings of poems about life, love and death, and Sibelius's heroically Nordic Fifth Symphony.

Anne Sofie von Otter

PROM 31

7.30pm – c9.25pm

Paul Patterson
Orchestra on Parade 4'
London premiere

Tippett
The Midsummer Marriage –
Ritual Dances 25'

interval

Elgar
Symphony No. 1 in A flat major 53'

**National Youth Orchestra
of Great Britain
Tadaaki Otaka** *conductor*

Tadaaki Otaka

Tadaaki Otaka harnesses the youthful talents of the National Youth Orchestra in a programme of English music featuring a recent work by the orchestra's Composer in Residence, a magical set of nature dances from centenary composer Michael Tippett's first opera and the work that announced Elgar's arrival as a symphonist.

📖 *'Anniversary Composers', pages 36–38; 'New Music' pages 50–57*

PRICE A 🆆🅿️

PROM 32

4.00pm – c6.15pm

Bobby McFerrin & Friends

Bobby McFerrin *vocalist*
African Children's Choir
Michael Wolff *piano*
and Impure Thoughts
Badal Roy *tablas*
Mike Clark *drums*
John B. Williams *bass*

Following his sensational Proms debut in 2003 (*see right*), charismatic multi-vocalist Bobby McFerrin is joined by jazz composer-pianist Michael Wolff and the

Michael Wolff

amazing young voices of the African Children's Choir for this Proms contribution to Africa 05, the nationwide festival of African culture.

African Children's Choir

There will be one interval

PRICE A 🆆🅿️ →

PROM 33

8.00pm – c10.00pm

Berg
Three Pieces for Orchestra, Op. 6 20'

interval

Mahler
Das klagende Lied (original version) 68'

Gweneth-Ann Jeffers *soprano*
Michelle DeYoung *mezzo-soprano*
Johan Botha *tenor*
Mark Delavan *baritone*

**The Boys of King's College,
Cambridge
BBC Symphony Chorus
BBC Symphony Orchestra
Donald Runnicles** *conductor*

Here heard in its original three-part form, Mahler's early fairy-tale cantata was, in his own words, 'the first work in which I became "Mahler"' and offers tantalising hints of the songs and symphonies to follow. The three

Donald Runnicles

early pieces by anniversary composer Alban Berg are also full of Mahlerian echoes, including a direct quote of the fateful hammer-blows from Mahler's Sixth Symphony (see Prom 63).

📖 *'Fairy Tales', pages 20–29; 'Anniversary Composers', pages 39–40*

PRICE A 🆆🅿️ ←

PROM 34

7.30pm – c9.55pm

Vaughan Williams
Fantasia on a Theme
by Thomas Tallis 16'

Tippett
Piano Concerto 34'

interval

Holst
The Planets 50'

concluding with
Colin Matthews
Pluto 7'

Steven Osborne *piano*

**New London Chamber Choir
BBC Scottish Symphony Orchestra
Martyn Brabbins** *conductor*

Vaughan Williams pays homage to Thomas Tallis (whose theme is heard in Prom 64) and a rising young British pianist gives a centenary performance of Tippett's Piano Concerto in an

Gustav Holst

all-English concert that concludes with Holst's popular astrological suite, as astronomically updated by Colin Matthews in 2000.

📖 *'Anniversary Composers', pages 36–38*

🎵 **1.00pm Proms Chamber Music**
See pages 114–117

🎙️ **6.00pm Pre-Prom Talk** (RAH)
Colin Matthews and Heather Couper

PRICE A

Gustav Holst by Herbert Lambert; drawings 'Schwind 'In the Forest'/Lebrecht Music & Arts (Holst)

PROM 35

7.30pm – c9.40pm

Lambert
Merchant Seamen – suite   11'

Coleridge-Taylor
Violin Concerto   32'

interval

Stanford
Songs of the Sea   18'

Elgar
Enigma Variations   30'

Philippe Graffin violin
Mark Stone baritone

The London Chorus
BBC Concert Orchestra
Barry Wordsworth conductor

In a feast of British music, highlights from a wartime film score by centenary composer Constant Lambert precede a rarely-heard concerto by Black British composer Samuel Coleridge-Taylor (played by the French violinist who has recently recorded it), a sea-songs suite by the Irish-born composer who conducted the premiere of Coleridge-Taylor's hugely successful *Hiawatha's Wedding Feast* and a coded celebration of friendship by the man who gave Coleridge-Taylor his first commission.

Coleridge-Taylor

📖 'The Sea', pages 4–13

🗨 **6.00pm Pre-Prom Talk** (RAH)
Philippe Graffin

PRICE A

PROM 36

7.30pm – c9.40pm

Weber
Der Freischütz – overture   10'

Unsuk Chin
snagS & Snarls   c25'
world premiere of new version

interval

Bruckner
Symphony No. 6 in A major   57'

Christiane Oelze soprano
Dagmar Pecková mezzo-soprano

Deutsches Sinfonie-Orchester Berlin
Kent Nagano conductor

Kent Nagano leads his Berlin orchestra for the first time at the Proms in Bruckner's sonorous Sixth Symphony, preceded by a magical Weber overture and a foretaste of Unsuk Chin's forthcoming opera based on Lewis Carroll's *Alice in Wonderland*.

📖 'New Music', pages 50–57

🗨 **6.00pm Pre-Prom Talk** (RAH)
Unsuk Chin

PRICE A

PROM 32

Bobby McFerrin & Friends

Two years after he got an entire Albert Hall audience singing along to the *Ave Maria*, the American multi-vocalist returns to front a Prom for Africa 05

He wrote the classic hit 'Don't Worry, Be Happy', and has wowed audiences around the world with his amazing vocal improvisations. Two years ago he made his Proms debut, dazzling a packed hall both with his vocal agility and with his conducting skill, not only powering the Vienna Philharmonic Orchestra through a selection of popular orchestral pieces but also getting them to sing the *William Tell* overture, and then coaxing the entire audience to sing along to Gounod's *Ave Maria* too.

Now Bobby McFerrin is back, in a Sunday-afternoon concert as part of the BBC's contribution to the UK-wide celebration of African culture, Africa 05. He'll be joined by jazz pianist Michael Wolff, a similarly eclectic musical magpie, and his trio Impure Thoughts. But central to the concert are the voices of the African Children's Choir, a group of talented 7- to 11-year-olds drawn from the orphaned and destitute children who are receiving their education at one of the several schools set up throughout Africa by their founder Ray Barnett.

With solo sets and collaborations between the groups – and a spot of audience participation too – it promises to be an inspirational musical melting-pot, and one of this year's most stirring Proms.

For more on Africa 05, visit bbc.co.uk/africa05

Every Prom live on BBC Radio 3 and bbc.co.uk/proms
Advance Booking from 16 May • General Booking from 13 June: 020 7589 8212

97

PROM 37
7.30pm – c9.30pm

Brahms
Tragic Overture   14'

Beethoven
Piano Concerto No. 4 in G major   36'

interval

Wagner
Lohengrin – Prelude to Act 1   9'

Hartmann
Symphony No. 6   24'

Gianluca Cascioli piano

BBC Symphony Orchestra
Ingo Metzmacher conductor

Ingo Metzmacher returns to the BBC SO to chart the Germanic tradition from Beethoven through Brahms and Wagner to centenary composer Karl Amadeus Hartmann, who bravely withdrew into 'internal exile' during the years of Nazi rule (see right). Italian pianist Gianluca Cascioli makes his Proms debut.

Wagnerian fairy-tale: Lohengrin, Elsa and the swan

🔊 **6.00pm Pre-Prom Talk** (RAH)
Introduction to K. A. Hartmann

 PRICE A

PROM 38
7.30pm – c9.45pm

Bent Sørensen
The Little Mermaid   c26'
BBC co-commission with Danish National Symphony Orchestra & Choirs/DR: world premiere

Grieg
Piano Concerto in A minor   27'

interval

Nielsen
Symphony No. 5   37'

Inger Dam-Jensen soprano
Gert Henning-Jensen tenor
Lars Vogt piano

Danish National Girls' Choir/DR
Danish National Radio Symphony Orchestra/DR
Thomas Dausgaard conductor

Danish conductor Thomas Dausgaard gives the world premiere of Bent Sørensen's dramatic re-telling of Hans Christian Andersen's most famous tale, interspersed with extracts from the author's diaries. Grieg's popular Piano Concerto – performed by brilliant German pianist Lars Vogt (who also gives a Proms Chamber recital on Monday 15 August) – and Nielsen's exhilarating Fifth Symphony complete an all-Scandinavian line-up.

📖 *'Fairy Tales', pages 20–29;*
'New Music', pages 50–57

🔊 **6.00pm Pre-Prom Talk** (RGS)
Bent Sørensen

PRICE A WP

PROM 39
7.00pm – c8.50pm

Mendelssohn
A Midsummer Night's Dream – incidental music *(sung in English)*   45'

interval

Beethoven
Symphony No. 5 in C minor   33'

Mary Nelson soprano
Victoria Simmonds mezzo-soprano

Methodist College Belfast Girls' Choir
Ulster Orchestra
Thierry Fischer conductor

Mendelssohn's incidental music to Shakespeare's magical dream-play takes centre-stage in this year's fairy-tale theme. After the interval, light triumphs over darkness as Thierry Fischer and the Ulster Orchestra follow up their successful Beethoven symphony cycle by reprising the Fifth, with its famous opening 'Victory V'.

📖 *'Fairy Tales', pages 20–29*

PRICE A WP →

PROM 40
10.00pm – c11.30pm

Africa 05

Baaba Maal
with **Daande Lenol**

Baaba Maal

Baaba Maal, the sensational Senegalese singer-songwriter and UN representative on the issue of HIV/Aids in Africa, brings his band Dande Lenol (Voice of the People) to the Proms for the first time in our season's second contribution to this year's nationwide Africa 05 celebrations. A man with a mission that extends beyond music – his latest album *Missing You ... Mi Yeewnii* includes songs calling for African unity and for the continent's leaders to accept responsibility for its troubles, as well as reminders of all that Africa has given to the world – Baaba sings to and for the people of Africa with a unique mix of traditional Senegalese and more recent Black American and Jamaican influences.

Baaba Maal

There will be no interval

PRICE E WP ←

PROM 41

6.30pm – c8.35pm

Mozart
Sinfonia concertante in E flat major, for oboe, clarinet, bassoon and horn, K297b *30'*

interval

Mahler
Symphony No. 1 in D major *55'*

West-Eastern Divan Orchestra
Daniel Barenboim conductor

Daniel Barenboim

Daniel Barenboim returns with his young orchestra of Arab and Israeli musicians – 'a paradigm of coherent and intelligent living together,' he calls it – with Mahler's titanic first symphony and a Mozart *sinfonia concertante* that aptly showcases soloists from the orchestra in a dialogue between two groups of musicians.

Broadcast on BBC2

 3.00pm Proms Films (RGS)
Eroica

 PRICE **A** WP

PROM 42

7.30pm – c10.00pm

Tchaikovsky
The Nutcracker – excerpts *c25'*

interval

Tchaikovsky
Iolanta (concert performance; sung in Russian) *95'*

Nuccia Focile *Iolanta*
Elizabeth Donovan *Brigitta*
Camilla Roberts *Laura*
Clare Shearer *Martha*
Peter Hoare *Vaudemont*
Ilya Bannik *King René*
Vladimir Moroz *Robert*
Pavel Baransky *Ebn-Hakir*
David Soar *Bertrand*
Ian Yemm *Almeric*

Orchestra and Chorus
of Welsh National Opera
Vassily Sinaisky conductor

Written as a one-act curtain-raiser to *The Nutcracker*, Tchaikovsky's *Iolanta* tells of a blind princess whose new-found love for a nobleman restores her sight. Tonight, history is reversed as excerpts from the ballet act as a prelude to a rare complete performance of the composer's final, fairy-tale opera.

Nuccia Focile

📖 'Fairy Tales', pages 20–29; 'Season Highlights', page 71

♪ **1.00pm Proms Chamber Music**
See pages 114–117

🔊 **6.00pm Pre-Prom Talk** (RAH)
Introduction to Tchaikovsky's *Iolanta*

 PRICE **A**

PROM 37

HARTMANN: Symphony No. 6

A member of the musical resistance to Hitler, Hartmann was also a major symphonist in the great Austro-German tradition. Ingo Metzmacher has long been one of his keenest champions

'It really takes off at the end, doesn't it?' The energy in Ingo Metzmacher's voice echoes that of the last movement of Karl Amadeus Hartmann's Sixth Symphony, which he brings to the Proms in the composer's centenary year. Metzmacher has long been a champion of 20th-century music: as Hamburg's General Music Director, he famously replaced the city's traditional New Year's Eve concerts with the provocatively titled 'Who's Afraid of 20th-Century Music?' series. He's especially championed Hartmann, who boldly refused to let his music be

Hartmann: German music's conscientious objector

performed in Nazi Germany, preferring to go into what he called 'inner exile'.

For Metzmacher – two of whose previous Proms appearances have been to conduct the UK premieres of Henze's Ninth and Tenth Symphonies – Hartmann is a natural continuation of the great Austro-German symphonic line. 'There have been many 20th-century symphonies, but very few composers have tried to conserve that tradition along the line of Haydn, Beethoven, Brahms, Bruckner and Mahler. And because Hartmann chose to live in a kind of self-imposed exile in his own land during the Nazi rule, he really suffered. On the one hand there's anger in his music, and on the other there's sorrow and suffering.'

Like all but the last two of his eight numbered symphonies, the Sixth reworks material originally written during the Nazi era. For Metzmacher, its unusual two-movement form suggests the slow movement and scherzo of a lost or imaginary larger-scale work – 'kept alive as a torso, with just these two precious inner movements'. The Adagio, he says, 'builds up slowly and carefully to a climax, after which the rest of the movement seems like fragments of memories, like broken glass', while the frenetic triple-fugue finale ends, as he reminds us, '*very* fast'.

Every Prom live on BBC Radio 3 and bbc.co.uk/proms
Advance Booking from 16 May • General Booking from 13 June: 020 7589 8212

99

PROM 43

7.30pm – c9.45pm

Stravinsky
Fireworks   4'

Marc-André Dalbavie
Piano Concerto   c30'
BBC co-commission with The Cleveland Orchestra and Chicago Symphony Orchestra: world premiere

interval

Shostakovich
Symphony No. 11 in G minor,
'The Year 1905'   65'

Leif Ove Andsnes *piano*

BBC Symphony Orchestra
Jukka-Pekka Saraste *conductor*

Jukka-Pekka Saraste

Rounding off his tenure as Principal Guest Conductor of the BBC SO, Jukka-Pekka Saraste premieres Marc-André Dalbavie's new piano concerto – performed by Norwegian pianist Leif Ove Andsnes. Stravinsky's early *jeu d'esprit* contrasts with Shostakovich's graphic symphony written for the 40th anniversary of the October Revolution and ostensibly looking back to the earlier failed uprising against the Tsar in 1905.

📖 *'New Music', pages 50–57*

🔊 **5.30pm Composer Portrait** (RAH)
Marc-André Dalbavie. See page 125

PRICE **A**

PROM 44

7.00pm – c9.05pm

Berg
Lulu Suite   32'

interval

Mahler
Symphony No. 4 in G major   60'

Christine Schäfer *soprano*

Royal Philharmonic Orchestra
Daniele Gatti *conductor*

One of Germany's leading sopranos, Christine Schäfer (*see right*) revisits the role of the seductive heroine of anniversary composer Alban Berg's unfinished second opera *Lulu* – in which she scored a big success at both Glyndebourne and the Proms in 1996 – before returning after the interval in more innocent mode to sing the child's-eye view of Heaven that ends Mahler's popular Fourth Symphony.

Christine Schäfer

📖 *'Anniversary Composers', pages 39–40*

PRICE **A** →

PROM 45

10.00pm – c11.30pm

Pérotin
Sederunt principes   12'

Arvo Pärt
An den Wassern   6'
Nunc dimittis   8'
Salve regina   11'
Trivium   7'
Dopo la vittoria   11'

interspersed with
plainchant and anonymous 12th-, 13th- and 14th-century French and English motets and monody

Christopher Bowers-Broadbent
organ

Estonian Philharmonic Chamber Choir
Paul Hillier *director*

The choral works of anniversary composer Arvo Pärt conceal a sensual core beyond their simple, spacious surfaces. No-one has worked in closer association with the composer than Paul Hillier, whose brilliant Estonian choir performs this music interspersed with the kind of early polyphony which Pärt studied before re-emerging in the 1970s with his bell-like ('tintinnabuli') style.

📖 *'Anniversary Composers', page 41*
There will be no interval

PRICE **D** ←

PROM 46

7.30pm – c9.35pm

Lilburn
Symphony No. 3   15'

Mahler
Des Knaben Wunderhorn –
selection   25'

interval

Sibelius
Symphony No. 2 in D major   44'

Jonathan Lemalu *bass-baritone*

New Zealand Symphony Orchestra
James Judd *conductor*

Jonathan Lemalu

New Zealand-born Samoan bass-baritone Jonathan Lemalu, a former BBC Radio 3 New Generation Artist, sings some of Mahler's settings from the German folk-poetry collection that fascinated him from his earliest works through to his Fourth Symphony. James Judd and the NZSO recorded all three symphonies by leading New Zealand composer Douglas Lilburn shortly before his death in 2001 and here perform the last – a one-movement work from 1961 – to mark his 90th anniversary. Their Proms debut concert ends with Sibelius's Second Symphony – an apparent evocation of Finnish woodlands, mainly composed in Italy.

📖 *'Fairy Tales', pages 20–29*

🔊 **6.00pm Pre-Prom Talk** (RAH)
Members of the New Zealand SO

PRICE **A**

PROM 47

7.00pm – c8.55pm

Tippett
Symphony No. 4 · 34'

interval

Beethoven
Symphony No. 3 in E flat major,
'Eroica' · 50'

London Symphony Orchestra
Sir Colin Davis conductor

Sir Colin Davis, one of Tippett's foremost champions, charts the birth-to-death scenario of the centenary composer's Fourth Symphony. The transition is reversed in Beethoven's epoch-making 'Eroica' Symphony, where the journey, despite its brooding funeral march, ends in a euphoric celebration of the greatness of mankind. Premiered 200 years ago, its first performance is recreated in Simon Cellan Jones's film *Eroica*, being shown in our Proms Films series on Sunday 14 August (see page 126).

'Anniversary Composers', pages 36–38

PROM 48

10.00pm – c11.25pm

Elgar
Serenade for Strings · 12'

Stuart MacRae
Hamartia (Cello Concerto) · 17'
London premiere

Nicholas Maw
Life Studies – Nos. 3, 6 & 8 · 14'

Shostakovich, arr. Rudolf Barshai
Chamber Symphony, Op. 110a · 25'

Li-Wei cello

Scottish Ensemble
Clio Gould director

Li-Wei

Three British works for strings – Elgar's ever-popular *Serenade*, a new cello concerto from Scottish composer Stuart MacRae (whose Violin Concerto was premiered at the 2001 Proms) and a 70th-anniversary sample of Nicholas Maw – preface a chamber arrangement of the self-referential string quartet (No. 8) that Shostakovich conceived in the ruins of Dresden and wrote 'in memory of the victims of fascism and war'.

1906·1975
Д. Д. ШОСТАКОВИЧ
Shostakovich: Russian commemorative stamp, 1975

'New Music', pages 50–57

There will be no interval

PROM 44

BERG: Lulu Suite

Innocent victim or *femme fatale*? **Christine Schäfer**, who sang the role of Lulu at the Proms in 1996 and returns this year to sing in the *Lulu Suite*, gives her view of Berg's enigmatic heroine

It was Christine Schäfer's performance in the title-role of Berg's opera *Lulu* – first at Glyndebourne and then at the Proms in 1996 – that launched her international operatic career. Still one of the world's leading interpreters of the part, she returns to the Proms this year to sing the central 'Song of Lulu' from the concert suite which Berg, knowing that performances of his opera would be unlikely within the Third Reich, designed as a calling-card to raise interest abroad.

In the opera – which Berg didn't live to complete, having interrupted work on it to write his deeply personal Violin Concerto (see Prom 55) – Lulu is introduced by a circus ringmaster as 'someone created to cause grief and pain, to lure and to seduce and to envenom', although in her own song she disclaims personal responsibility for the deadly consequences of her universal allure.

Schäfer sees her more as an innocent victim around whom men happen to lose their senses, rather than the subversive temptress famously incarnated by Louise Brooks in G. W. Pabst's silent films of the original Wedekind plays. 'There's nothing dirty about Lulu in Berg's view, so it's difficult to present her as a *femme fatale*. Her music is very honest and she always says what she's thinking. When playing Lulu, you are in the middle of everything, and yet not really part of it.'

There's a disembodied quality too to 'Das himmlische Leben' ('Heavenly Life'), the orchestral song closing Mahler's Fourth Symphony, which Schäfer sings in the same Prom. The paradise here – where 'bread is baked by angels' and the music is created by St Cecilia herself – is in sharp contrast to the earthly suffering caused, knowingly or otherwise, by Berg's Lulu.

Every Prom live on BBC Radio 3 and bbc.co.uk/proms
Advance Booking from 16 May · General Booking from 13 June: 020 7589 8212

PRICE A

PRICE D

101

SATURDAY 20 AUGUST	SUNDAY 21 AUGUST	MONDAY 22 AUGUST	TUESDAY 23 AUGUST

PROM 49

7.30pm – c9.35pm

PROM 50

6.30pm – c8.30pm

PROM 51

7.30pm – c9.45pm

PROM 52

6.00pm – c10.35pm

Sofia Gubaidulina
The Light of the End   24'
UK premiere

interval

Beethoven
Symphony No. 9 in D minor,
'Choral'   70'

Christine Goerke *soprano*
Carolin Masur *mezzo-soprano*
Thomas Studebaker *tenor*
Hanno Müller-Brachmann
bass-baritone

Finchley Children's Music Group
London Philharmonic Choir
London Philharmonic Orchestra
Kurt Masur *conductor*

Kurt Masur directs the annual Proms performance of Beethoven's life-affirming 'Choral' Symphony, preceded by a work commissioned by the Boston Symphony Orchestra from Sofia Gubaidulina, whose highly individual orchestral writing employs large forces for the sake of colour rather than volume.

📖 'New Music', pages 50–57
Broadcast on BBC2

🔲 **6.00pm Pre-Prom Talk** (RAH)
Sofia Gubaidulina

Novák
Eternal Longing   20'

Schumann
Piano Concerto in A minor   32'

interval

Stravinsky
The Firebird – suite (1945)   30'

Llŷr Williams *piano*

BBC Symphony Orchestra
Jiří Bělohlávek *conductor*

The BBC SO's Czech-born Chief Conductor Designate continues our exploration of fairy tales with an evocative Andersen-inspired allegory by fellow Czech Vítězslav Novák and Stravinsky's kaleidoscopic breakthrough ballet *The Firebird*. Llŷr Williams, one of Britain's fastest-rising pianists and a current BBC Radio 3 New Generation Artist, performs Schumann's giant among Romantic piano concertos.

Jiří Bělohlávek

📖 'Fairy Tales', pages 20–29

🎞 **3.00pm Proms Films** (RGS)
Holocaust: A Music Memorial Film

🔲 **c8.45pm Post-Prom Event**
(WAF) *The Encore. See page 125*

Ravel
Alborada del gracioso   9'

Piano Concerto in G major   22'

interval

Shostakovich
Symphony No. 8 in C minor   65'

Hélène Grimaud *piano*

London Symphony Orchestra
Bernard Haitink *conductor*

Following last year's 75th-birthday appearances, Bernard Haitink returns with the London Symphony Orchestra to display two sides of Ravel's musical personality: dapper, urbane and jazzy in the Piano Concerto – performed by

Hélène Grimaud

Proms favourite Hélène Grimaud – and at his most exaggeratedly parodic in his own orchestration of a Spanish-flavoured piano piece. Shostakovich's Eighth Symphony, written at the height of World War II, presents a highly personal response to mass devastation.

🎵 **1.00pm Proms Chamber Music**
See pages 114–117

Handel
Julius Caesar *(semi-staged;
sung in Italian)*   215'

Glyndebourne Festival Opera

Sarah Connolly *Caesar*
Patricia Bardon *Cornelia*
Angelika Kirchschlager *Sextus*
Rosemary Joshua *Cleopatra*
Christophe Dumaux *Ptolemy*
Christopher Maltman *Achillas*
Rachid ben Abdeslam *Nirenus*
Alexander Ashworth *Curius*

Glyndebourne Festival Chorus
**Orchestra of the Age of
Enlightenment**
William Christie *conductor*

Arguably the finest of all Handel's operas, *Julius Caesar* comes to the Proms in a special semi-staging of this summer's new Glyndebourne Festival production (directed by David McVicar) with a cast

Sarah Connolly

headed by leading British mezzo-soprano Sarah Connolly and reuniting the formidable combination of William Christie and the Orchestra of the Age of Enlightenment.

📖 'Season Highlights', page 72
There will be two 20-minute intervals

🔲 **4.30pm Pre-Prom Talk** (RAH)
Introduction to Handel's *Julius Caesar*

PRICE **B**   PRICE **A**   PRICE **B**   PRICE **B**

PROM 53
7.00pm – c8.50pm

Ravel
Rapsodie espagnole   15'

Shéhérazade   16'

interval

Walton
Symphony No. 1 in B flat minor   43'

Bernarda Fink *mezzo-soprano*

European Union Youth Orchestra
Sir John Eliot Gardiner *conductor*

Sir John Eliot Gardiner directs the pan-European orchestra of young virtuosos in two contrasting works by Ravel: one of the half-Basque composer's most exuberant tributes to Spain and his ecstatic salute to the exotic mysteries of the East, sung by Argentine mezzo-soprano Bernarda Fink. After the interval, Walton's explosively intense but long-gestated First Symphony – in the composer's words, 'the climax of my youth' – is revived 70 years after the BBC gave its first performance.

Bernarda Fink

PROM 54
10.00pm – c11.05pm

Henryk Górecki
Symphony No. 3, 'Symphony of Sorrowful Songs'   60'

Susan Bullock *soprano*

BBC Scottish Symphony Orchestra
David Atherton *conductor*

In his emergence from the 1960s avant-garde into a more warmly expressive and pared-down style that embraced older musical and spiritual traditions, the Polish composer Henryk Górecki – like his Estonian counterpart Arvo Pärt (see Prom 45) – perhaps inadvertently helped create a wave of 'faith minimalism' that has won new audiences for classical music around the world. An international best-seller when released on CD a dozen years ago, his Third Symphony, whose central text harks back to the events of World War II, is here revived as part of our commemoration for that conflict's end 60 years ago (see *right*).

Henryk Górecki

There will be no interval

PROM 54
GÓRECKI: Symphony No. 3

Soprano Susan Bullock is the soloist in a Late Night performance of the Polish composer's hauntingly popular 'sorrowful' symphony

Polish composer Henryk Górecki's Third Symphony takes the unusual form of three slow movements, each of them painting a picture in song of a mother's relationship to a lost child. The first song draws on a 15th-century version of Mary's lamentation at the foot of the Cross, in which the Virgin prays to share her son's wounds. The second song sets lines found scratched on her cell wall by 18-year-old Helena Wanda Blazusiakówna, a wartime prisoner at Gestapo HQ in Zakopane: 'Mother, do not weep.' And the words of the final song describe a peasant mother mourning the loss of her soldier son in World War I.

In the words of soprano Susan Bullock, who returns to sing Górecki's 'sorrowful songs' at this year's Proms following her Messiaen performance last year, 'It's an amazing, mesmeric piece that starts from nothing and builds gradually until the intensity is almost unbearable.'

'When I performed it for the first time, in Bilbao,' she recalls, 'it had a huge effect on the audience. Some of them found it deeply moving, almost disturbing, while others just wafted along in this wonderful wash of string sound.'

While the whole piece has enjoyed huge worldwide success ever since the London Sinfonietta's recording first stormed the Classical charts in the early 1990s, the second movement has tended to be the most popular, often being excerpted out and played on its own. Bullock disapproves of treating it in this way – 'almost like a pop song. The whole piece deserves a fair reckoning,' she insists; 'it's all part of one great big arch.'

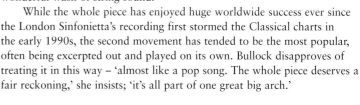
Susan Bullock

Every Prom live on BBC Radio 3 and bbc.co.uk/proms
Advance Booking from 16 May • General Booking from 13 June: 020 7589 8212

PRICE **A**

PRICE **D**

PROM 56

BRAHMS: Violin Concerto

The concerto may be standard rep but, says **Nikolaj Znaider**, that doesn't lessen either its emotional power or its technical challenge

Born to Polish-Israeli parents, Danish violinist Nikolaj Znaider won the Carl Nielsen International Violin Competition and studied at New York's Juilliard School before becoming uncertain of his playing and deciding to rebuild his technique from scratch – almost literally – in Vienna. In 1997 the painful work paid off, when he won the prestigious Queen Elisabeth Competition in Brussels. Having performed Nielsen's concerto at the 2002 Proms, he returns this year to play Brahms's great Romantic concerto, written for the Hungarian violinist Joseph Joachim.

A contemporary of Brahms famously quipped that if Bruch's concerto had been written for the violin, Brahms's was written *against* it; while Bronislaw Huberman (whose violin Joshua Bell brings to the Proms this year, *see page 91*) later added that the work was rather composed 'for the violin *against* the orchestra – and the violin wins!'

It's not a view that Znaider shares: 'As with Beethoven's concerto, the solo violin doesn't dominate throughout the whole work. There's a balance between when the violin is the principal voice and when it is accompanying or commenting on the orchestral music, particularly in the first movement.'

Brahms's expressively lyrical writing dominates the slow movement. 'Emotionally, it seems to speak to everyone,' says Znaider, pointing out that the difficulty here is that the violin line has to be sustained, even when it's not the centre of attention. 'Then there's the Hungarian touch in the finale, as often in Brahms, with an attractive, very virtuosic Rondo.'

As for the work's technical difficulties, time, he feels, has not diminished them: 'I think we all have to fight a little – they were accomplished players too in those days. It's a difficult piece, surely, but more in the sense of trying to create a sense of wholeness across its nearly 40-minute span.'

PROM 55

7.30pm – c9.25pm

Morgan Hayes
Strip   c12'
BBC commission: world premiere

Berg
Violin Concerto   27'

interval

Beethoven
Symphony No. 7 in A major   40'

Leonidas Kavakos *violin*

BBC Symphony Orchestra
Sir Andrew Davis *conductor*

Leonidas Kavakos

The BBC SO's Conductor Laureate introduces the first Proms commission from Morgan Hayes, in which the composer quotes from two of his favourite Proms commissions of past years. Anniversary composer Alban Berg's last completed work was dedicated 'to the memory of an angel' – the 18-year-old daughter of Mahler's widow Alma and the architect Walter Gropius. The concert closes with the Beethoven symphony that Wagner famously dubbed 'the apotheosis of the dance'.

📖 *'Anniversary Composers', pages 39–40; 'New Music', pages 50–57*

🔊 **6.00pm Pre-Prom Talk** (RAH)
Morgan Hayes

PROM 56

7.30pm – c9.40pm

Brahms
Violin Concerto in D major   38'

interval

Liszt
A Faust Symphony (original version)   62'

Nikolaj Znaider *violin*

BBC Philharmonic
Gianandrea Noseda *conductor*

Following his Proms debut in 2002, Danish-born virtuoso Nikolaj Znaider returns for one of the most lyrical of all violin concertos (*see left*). Gianandrea Noseda, who has forged a unique partnership with the BBC Philharmonic, also leads Franz Liszt's symphonic take on the Faust legend – a particularly apt subject for the great composer-pianist who, like the violin virtuoso Paganini before him, was rumoured to have sold his soul to the devil.

Mariano Fortuny y Marsal: *A Faust Fantasy*, 1866

📖 *'Season Highlights', page 73*

🔊 **6.00pm Pre-Prom Talk** (RAH)
Introduction to Liszt's *A Faust Symphony*

 PRICE **A**

 PRICE **A**

SATURDAY 27 AUGUST

PROM 57

7.30pm – c9.45pm

Rossini
William Tell – overture *12'*

Debussy
Prélude à l'après-midi d'un faune *10'*

Esa-Pekka Salonen
new work *c7'*
BBC commission: world premiere

Wagner
The Mastersingers of Nuremberg – Prelude to Act I *10'*

interval

Rimsky-Korsakov
Sheherazade *45'*

World Orchestra for Peace
Valery Gergiev *conductor*

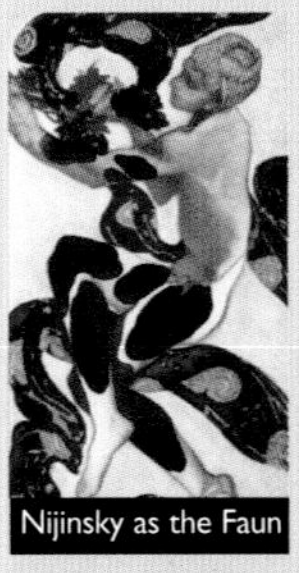

Nijinsky as the Faun

The orchestra that the late Georg Solti founded as music's 'ambassadors for peace' (*see right*) offers a catalogue of orchestral showpieces under its current Music Director, Valery Gergiev, as part of its 'Credit Suisse Tour 2005'. Alongside operatic extracts by Rossini and Wagner, Debussy's evocation of a faun's erotic dream and Rimsky-Korsakov's *Arabian Nights* fantasy, there's a new work by Finnish composer-conductor Esa-Pekka Salonen, whose music has featured regularly over recent Proms seasons.

'Fairy Tales', pages 20–29; 'New Music', pages 50–57

Broadcast on BBC2

PRICE C

SUNDAY 28 AUGUST

PROM 58

6.30pm – c8.00pm

Verdi
Requiem *85'*

Barbara Frittoli *soprano*
Daniela Barcellona *mezzo-soprano*
Giuseppe Filianoti *tenor*
Ferruccio Furlanetto *bass*

BBC Symphony Chorus
City of Birmingham Symphony Chorus
BBC Philharmonic
Gianandrea Noseda *conductor*

Gianandrea Noseda, the Italian-born Principal Conductor of the BBC Philharmonic, brings an authentically all-Italian cast to this performance of the most operatically Italianate of Requiems.

Giuseppe Verdi: portrait by Giovanni Boldini, 1886

'Season Highlights', page 74

There will be no interval

PRICE B

MONDAY 29 AUGUST

PROM 59

7.30pm – c9.35pm

Wagner
The Flying Dutchman – overture *10'*

Beethoven
Piano Concerto No. 3 in C minor *36'*

interval

R. Strauss
Also sprach Zarathustra *34'*

Emanuel Ax *piano*

Tonhalle Orchestra, Zurich
David Zinman *conductor*

Emanuel Ax

In a welcome return for Zurich's Tonhalle Orchestra, following its Proms debut in 2003, the tempestuous seascape of *The Flying Dutchman* overture contrasts with the sunburst opening of Strauss's loftiest tone-poem, while one of the world's best-loved pianists returns to the Proms to play one of Beethoven's most Mozartian concertos.

'The Sea', pages 4–13

Recorded for later broadcast on BBC1

1.00pm Proms Chamber Music
See pages 114–117

PRICE B

PROM 57

WORLD ORCHESTRA FOR PEACE

Not just playing for time, but playing for peace in our time

Founded by Georg Solti for the 50th anniversary of the UN in 1995, the World Orchestra for Peace comprises players from leading professional orchestras around the world. 'We are about 40 nations in this orchestra,' said Solti at the time of its debut, 'and we live in such harmony, playing so beautifully; we prove that we can live in peace. I wish politicians, left and right, could do the same.' On Solti's death in 1997, the baton passed to Valery Gergiev, who shares Solti's passionate belief in music as a uniting force. Following appearances at the Baden-Baden Festival, the BBC Proms in 2000 and the Stars of the White Nights festival, this unique ensemble reconvenes this year to mark the 60th anniversary of the end of World War II.

Valery Gergiev

... Images (Verdi); J. Henry Fair (Ax); Lebrecht Music & Arts ('Flying Dutchman'); Chris Christodoulou (Gergiev)

PROM 60

7.00pm – c8.45pm

Mahler
Symphony No. 3 in D minor   95'

Yvonne Naef *mezzo-soprano*

Trinity Boys' Choir
The Cleveland Orchestra Chorus
(women's voices)
The Cleveland Orchestra
Franz Welser-Möst *conductor*

In his first appearance at the Proms since becoming Music Director of the Cleveland Orchestra, Franz Welser-Möst tackles Mahler's most ambitious and pantheistic symphony – a work in which the composer sought to give 'the whole of nature a voice' (from the beasts and flowers right up to God himself) and whose fourth movement sets lines from the same Nietzschean text that inspired Strauss's *Also sprach Zarathustra* (performed in Prom 59).

Friedrich Nietzsche: the voice of Zarathustra

There will be no interval

PRICE **C** →

PROM 61

10.00pm – c11.30pm

Stravinsky
Symphonies of Wind Instruments
(1920 version)   11'

Pierre Boulez
cummings ist der Dichter   13'

Stravinsky
The Dove Descending; Pater noster;
Ave Maria; Credo   11'

Messiaen
Trois petites liturgies de
la Présence Divine   34'

Nicolas Hodges *piano*
Cynthia Millar *ondes martenot*

BBC Singers
BBC Symphony Orchestra
David Robertson *conductor*

The BBC SO's Principal Guest Conductor Designate marks the 80th birthday of Pierre Boulez, whose Ensemble Intercontemporain he conducted from 1992 to 2000. The *Trois petites liturgies* of Boulez's teacher Messiaen were first performed 60 years ago, in newly liberated Paris. Sacred choral pieces by Stravinsky, and the Russian composer's memorial tribute to Debussy, complete this late-night programme.

David Robertson

Pierre Boulez

There will be no interval

PRICE **D** ←

PROM 62

7.30pm – c9.00pm

Beethoven
Missa solemnis (Mass in D major)   80'

Emily Magee *soprano*
Yvonne Naef *mezzo-soprano*
Jonas Kaufmann *tenor*
Franz-Josef Selig *bass*

The Cleveland Orchestra Chorus
The Cleveland Orchestra
Franz Welser-Möst *conductor*

'From the heart: may it reach to the heart.' So reads Beethoven's dedication of his *Missa solemnis* – a powerful personal statement of his belief in the spirit of man and a work whose uncompromising nature makes it a challenge as great as any in the choral repertory.

Franz Welser-Möst

'Season Highlights', page 75
There will be no interval

PRICE **C**

PROM 63

7.00pm – c8.35pm

Mahler
Symphony No. 6 in A minor   85'

Royal Concertgebouw Orchestra
Mariss Jansons *conductor*

At the beginning of his auspicious partnership with Amsterdam's Royal Concertgebouw Orchestra (see *right*), Mariss Jansons conducts Mahler's massive Sixth Symphony – a work whose fateful hammer blows seemed to prophesy the early death of the composer's daughter, the loss of his post at the Vienna Court Opera and the diagnosis of his own fatal heart condition.

Gustav Mahler: anonymous portrait, c1905

There will be no interval

PRICE **C** →

PROM 64

10.00pm – c11.15pm

Wylkynson
Credo in Deum / Jesus autem   6'

Cornysh
Salve regina   14'

Tallis
Nine Tunes for Archbishop Parker's
Psalter   10'

O nata lux de lumine   2'

Gaude gloriosa Dei mater   17'

Spem in alium   10'

The Sixteen
Harry Christophers conductor

Early English music in the late evening,
featuring Thomas Tallis's nine hymn-tunes
for Archbishop Parker's Psalter (1567), of
which 'Why fum'th in sight?' was
memorably transformed by Vaughan
Williams over 300 years later in his
Fantasia on a Theme by Thomas Tallis (see
Prom 34). The evening reaches its climax
as Tallis's magnificent 40-part motet *Spem
in alium* resounds around the Royal
Albert Hall's rotunda.

📖 'Anniversary Composers', page 43
There will be no interval

PROM 65

7.30pm – c9.25pm

Lutoslawski
Concerto for Orchestra   30'

interval

Brahms
Symphony No. 1 in C minor   46'

Royal Concertgebouw Orchestra
Mariss Jansons conductor

Like Bartók in Hungary before him, Polish
composer Witold Lutoslawski turned to
the folk music of his country as a source
of inspiration; and, like Bartók too, he
incorporated folk material into his own
Concerto for Orchestra. The shadow of
Beethoven loomed heavily over Brahms,
resulting in the 15-year gestation of his
First Symphony.

Witold Lutoslawski

PROMS 63 & 65

MARISS JANSONS & the Concertgebouw

For Latvian maestro Mariss Jansons, going Dutch doesn't mean
going it alone, but going to a whole new level of meaning

During his 21 years as its Chief
Conductor, Mariss Jansons transformed
the international profile of the Oslo
Philharmonic Orchestra. For seven years
until 2003 he was also Music Director of
the Pittsburgh Symphony, which he
brought to the Proms in 2003. And last
year saw his memorable Proms debut
concerts as the new Chief Conductor
of the Munich-based Bavarian Radio
Symphony Orchestra. Since then
Jansons has taken on another jewel in
Europe's orchestral crown, the Royal
Concertgebouw Orchestra of Amsterdam.
He wasn't looking for another position –
the annual 10-week period with his
Munich ensemble would have let him
take on more guest-conducting
commitments – but, as he has said, 'when
the Concertgebouw comes to you, how
can you say no?'

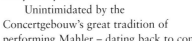
Mariss Jansons

Unintimidated by the
Concertgebouw's great tradition of
performing Mahler – dating back to concerts conducted by the composer
himself – Jansons brings the tragic Sixth Symphony in his first concert, and
pairs Lutoslawski's showpiece *Concerto for Orchestra* with Brahms's First
Symphony in the second.

Renowned as a meticulous orchestral technician, and demanding in
rehearsal, Jansons is nevertheless mindful of the larger picture. 'Imagination
is what players expect from a conductor,' he believes. 'You must give them
what is behind the notes – which is atmosphere, imagination and content. To
play the notes is not interesting. But what it *means*, the cosmic level at which
they are detached from problems of playing, that is my job as a conductor.'

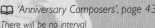

Every Prom live on BBC Radio 3 and bbc.co.uk/proms
Advance Booking from 16 May • General Booking from 13 June: 020 7589 8212

107

PROM 66
7.00pm – c9.05pm

PROM 67
6.30pm – c9.00pm

PROM 68
7.00pm – c8.55pm

PROM 69
7.00pm – c9.00pm

Copland
Fanfare for the Common Man   4'

Vaughan Williams
Symphony No. 6 in E minor   34'

interval

Berlioz
Symphonie fantastique   50'

Juilliard Orchestra
Orchestra of the
Royal Academy of Music
Sir Colin Davis conductor

Sir Colin Davis

In this major collaboration between
student musicians from New York's Juilliard
School and London's Royal Academy of
Music, Sir Colin Davis conducts a blazing
patriotic fanfare from the 'Dean of
American Music' and a wartime work that
Vaughan Williams always denied was his
'War Symphony', before ending with a
youthful dream-fantasy by the French
composer with whom Sir Colin is still
perhaps most closely associated.

Broadcast on BBC2

🗨 **5.30pm Pre-Prom Talk** (RAH)
Curtis Price and Joseph Polisi

Zemlinsky
Die Seejungfrau
(The Little Mermaid)   42'

interval

Brahms
A German Requiem   75'

Marie Arnet soprano
Bo Skovhus baritone

BBC Symphony Chorus
Philharmonia Chorus
BBC Symphony Orchestra
James Conlon conductor

James Conlon contrasts Zemlinsky's three-
movement orchestral fantasy after Hans
Christian Andersen with Brahms's great
vernacular Requiem, written in memory
both of his mother and of his great friend
and early supporter, Robert Schumann.

📖 *'Fairy Tales', pages 20–29;*
'Season Highlights', page 76
Broadcast on BBC4

🗨 **5.00pm Pre-Prom Talk** (RAH)
Introduction to *Die Seejungfrau*

Britten
Peter Grimes – Four Sea Interludes   17'

Rawsthorne
Piano Concerto No. 2   27'

interval

Tchaikovsky
Symphony No. 4 in F minor   36'

Howard Shelley piano

BBC National Orchestra of Wales
Rumon Gamba conductor

Alan Rawsthorne

Britten's four interludes
from his opera *Peter
Grimes* – premiered a
month after VE Day –
continue our sea
theme, and centenary
composer Alan
Rawsthorne's Second
Piano Concerto
returns to the Proms
for the first time in 20 years (see *right*).
Rumon Gamba, a regular guest with the
BBC orchestras, completes the evening
with Tchaikovsky's powerful 'Fate'
Symphony.

📖 *'The Sea', pages 4–13*
Broadcast on BBC4

🎵 **1.00pm Proms Chamber Music**
See pages 114–117

🗨 **5.15pm Audience Forum** (RAH)

Beethoven
Overture 'Namensfeier'   7'

Stravinsky
Pulcinella – suite   23'

Thomas Adès
Violin Concerto   c17'
UK premiere

interval

Beethoven
Symphony No. 4 in B flat major   34'

Anthony Marwood violin

Chamber Orchestra of Europe
Thomas Adès conductor

Acclaimed young British composer-
conductor Thomas Adès brings his new
Violin Concerto to the UK with the
orchestra and soloist who will just have
given its world premiere in Berlin. The
concert also includes music from
Stravinsky's first neo-Classical ballet
(based on music he thought was by
Pergolesi) and an overture and symphony
by Beethoven
that find their
composer in
lighter than
usual spirits.

Anthony Marwood

📖 *'New Music', pages 50–57*
Broadcast on BBC4

PROM 70

10.00pm – c11.30pm

Tippett
Dance, Clarion Air   5'

David Horne
Splintered Instruments   11'

Tippett
Four Songs from the British Isles   14'
Over the Sea to Skye   4'
London premiere

Elliott Carter
Mosaic   10'

Tippett, arr. Meirion Bowen
The Tempest – suite   25'

Mark Padmore *tenor*
David Wilson-Johnson *bass-baritone*

BBC Singers
Stephen Cleobury *conductor*

Nash Ensemble
Martyn Brabbins *conductor*

Having recently recorded a CD of Tippett choral works, the BBC Singers round off our centenary celebration of the composer with some familiar and less familiar pieces, including a recently discovered setting of the Skye boat-song, which, like the *Tempest* suite, links into our season's sea theme. The programme is completed by two instrumental works that the Nash Ensemble premiered as part of its 40th-anniversary season earlier this year.

📖 *'The Sea', pages 4–13; 'Anniversary Composers', pages 36–38*
There will be no interval

PROM 71

7.30pm – c9.35pm

Haydn
Symphony No. 103 in E flat major,
'Drumroll'   30'

Berg
Three Fragments from 'Wozzeck'   20'

interval

Stravinsky
The Rite of Spring   33'

Katarina Dalayman *soprano*

Vienna Philharmonic Orchestra
Zubin Mehta *conductor*

A drumroll from Haydn introduces a rare London appearance by Zubin Mehta in the first of the Vienna Philharmonic's two Proms appearances this season. Our Berg centenary survey closes with the concert suite the composer made from his first opera *Wozzeck*, featuring the Swedish soprano who recently sang the role of Marie in the complete work at Covent Garden. And the concert ends with the climactic ritual sacrifice of Stravinsky's pagan ballet *The Rite of Spring*.

Zubin Mehta

📖 *'Anniversary Composers', pages 39–40*
Broadcast on BBC4

PROM 68

RAWSTHORNE: Piano Concerto No. 2

Howard Shelley marks the Lancashire-born composer's centenary by reviving the concerto he wrote for the Festival of Britain in 1951

A pianist of chameleon-like versatility – equally at home in the concertos of Rakhmaninov and Gershwin, or exploring the highways and byways of the Classical and Romantic periods, whether at the keyboard or, increasingly, as a conductor – Howard Shelley has appeared at the Proms over a dozen times since making his debut in 1972, aged only 22. He's back again this year to perform Alan Rawsthorne's Second Piano Concerto, marking the birth-centenary of this now-neglected Lancashire-born composer.

Written at the height of postwar optimism for the Festival of Britain in 1951, its first soloist was the much-loved Clifford Curzon. 'He was an enormous inspiration to me as a youngster,' remembers Shelley, 'especially for the beauty of his sound and his amazingly deep musical insight. This concerto reflects some of that beauty and sensitivity. The charming opening, with the piano accompanying a flute solo, is a delicious start for a concerto, and the whole thing is very well structured, and contrasting in its moods. There's a constant to-ing and fro-ing between the sweetness and a more gritty, determined and muscular type of writing. It's still in the mould of the great Romantic tradition, in that the piano enters into argument, dialogue and discussion with the orchestra – unlike some later British piano concertos, where the piano is almost an additional colour to the orchestra.'

Back in 1985, Shelley heard John Ogdon play this concerto at the Proms. He never suspected that 20 years later he would perform the same work for what Rawsthorne himself once referred to as 'the most remarkable audience in the world'.

PROM 72

7.30pm – c9.05pm

Bruckner
Symphony No. 8 in C minor
(ed. Novak)   85'

Vienna Philharmonic Orchestra
Christoph Eschenbach *conductor*

One of the most sustained achievements
in the whole symphonic repertory is here
performed by one of the world's greatest
orchestras under leading conductor
Christoph Eschenbach.

There will be no interval
Broadcast on BBC4

PROM 73

7.30pm – c9.35pm

Debussy
La mer   24'

Mark-Anthony Turnage
From the Wreckage   c20'
BBC co-commission with Helsinki
Philharmonic and Gothenburg
Symphony orchestras: UK premiere

interval

Sibelius
Luonnotar   9'

Ravel
Daphnis and Chloë –
Suites Nos. 1 & 2   28'

Solveig Kringelborn *soprano*
Håkan Hardenberger *trumpet*

Crouch End Festival Chorus
Helsinki Philharmonic Orchestra
Esa-Pekka Salonen *conductor*

Debussy's impressionistic seascape
celebrates its centenary alongside
Sibelius's vocal evocation of the water-
borne earth-mother of Finnish mythology,
the two suites from Ravel's pastoral-
piratical ballet *Daphnis and Chloë*
(featuring the most keenly anticipated
sunrise in all music) and – fresh from this
year's Helsinki Festival – Mark-Anthony
Turnage's new work for Swedish trumpet
virtuoso Håkan Hardenberger.

📖 *'The Sea', pages 4–13; 'New Music',*
pages 50–57
Broadcast on BBC4

🔊 **6.00pm Pre-Prom Talk** (RAH)
Mark-Anthony Turnage

PROM 74

7.30pm – c10.35pm

THE LAST NIGHT OF THE PROMS 2005

Walton
Overture 'Portsmouth Point'   6'

Handel
Xerxes – 'Ombra mai fu'; Rodelinda –
'Dove sei'; Giustino – 'Se parla nel
mio cor'   12'

Rodrigo
Concierto de Aranjuez   22'

Lambert
The Rio Grande   15'

interval

Korngold
The Sea Hawk – suite   6'

Simon Bainbridge
Scherzi   6'

Purcell
King Arthur – 'Fairest Isle'   4'

Trad.
Down by the Salley Gardens   4'

Elgar
Pomp and Circumstance March No. 1   8'

Henry Wood
Fantasia on British Sea-Songs
(with additional numbers,
arr. Bob Chilcott)   23'

Parry, orch. Elgar
Jerusalem   2'

The National Anthem   2'

Auld Lang Syne   2'

Andreas Scholl *counter-tenor*
John Williams *guitar*
Paul Lewis *piano*
Louise Winter *mezzo-soprano*

BBC Singers
BBC Symphony Chorus
BBC Symphony Orchestra
Paul Daniel *conductor*

A seaborne Last Night with Walton,
Lambert and Korngold setting the
nautical scene for the centenary of
Henry Wood's *Sea-Songs* with their
original bugle calls restored. Andreas
Scholl is the first counter-tenor to
appear on the Last Night; he sings
Handel and Purcell, while guitar
legend John Williams plays Rodrigo
in a feast of music-making – joined
by Proms in the Park audiences
around the country – led by Last
Night debutant conductor Paul Daniel.

Andreas Scholl

John Williams

Paul Daniel

📖 *'The Sea', pages 4–13*
Broadcast on BBC2 (Part 1) and BBC1 (Part 2)

PROMS IN THE PARK

Hyde Park, London

Terry Wogan *presenter*
Andrea Bocelli *tenor*
Nicola Benedetti *violin*

THE
ROYAL
PARKS

**Further names
to be announced in May**

BBC Concert Orchestra
Carl Davis *conductor*

Carl Davis and the orchestra are joined
by Italian tenor Andrea Bocelli, who has
overcome blindness to establish a major
international career and teenage violin
sensation Nicola Benedetti, who last year
won BBC Young Musician of the Year
aged only 16 and already has her first
CD out. As ever, your host for the
evening is the inimitable and irrepressible
Mr Terry Wogan.

Gates open 4.00pm.
Entertainment on stage from 5.30pm.

For corporate hospitality facilities,
call Charles Webb on 0870 720 3010.

Event sponsored by

Lloyds TSB

Tickets: £20.00 (under-3s free),
available now by post/fax using the
Booking Form (*facing page 142*),
by phone on 0870 899 8100
(24 hours, national rate) or online at
bbc.co.uk/proms, and also (after 13 June)
from the Royal Albert Hall on 020 7589
8212 (9.00am–9.00pm).
A £2.25 transaction fee applies.

Tickets can also be bought in person (no
transaction fee) from the BBC Shops at
50 Margaret Street, London W1 and
Bush House, Strand, London WC2.

BBC Proms in the Park: 10th Anniversary Season

The BBC presents the 10th season of Proms in the Park, once again
bringing the unique festive atmosphere of the Last Night of the Proms
simultaneously to audiences in all four nations of the UK. As ever, all five
BBC Proms in the Park events – in London, Belfast, Glasgow, Manchester and
Swansea – will culminate in live big-screen link-ups with the Royal Albert Hall,
giving the whole country the chance to join in with the traditional singalong sequence of national songs.

Carl Davis

Terry Wogan

BBC Proms in the Park continues to offer a colourful conclusion to the season's programme, attracting
capacity audiences to outdoor venues across the country, where they come to picnic, participate and share
in the electric atmosphere and stunning live music-making of this unique national event.

**BBC
PROMS
in the Park**

This year's concerts are broadcast live
across BBC Radio and Television: BBC
Radio 2 broadcasts from London's Hyde
Park; BBC Radio Ulster, BBC Radio
Scotland, BBC GMR and BBC Radio Wales
broadcast their local events from Belfast,
Glasgow, Manchester and Swansea.
Highlights of all five Proms in the Park
concerts will be included as part of the
live coverage of the Last Night on BBC1
and BBC2, while Digital TV viewers can
choose between watching proceedings

inside the Royal Albert Hall and the
various Proms in the Park concerts taking
place across the UK.

*Note that all BBC Proms in the Park events are outdoors
and tickets are unreserved. The use of chairs is
discouraged since it obstructs the
view of others, but if you find it
necessary because of limited
mobility, please be considerate
to your neighbours. In the interest
of safety, please do not bring
glass items, barbecues or
flaming torches.*

Andrea Bocelli

Nicola Benedetti

**For BBC Proms in the Park concerts
in Belfast, Glasgow, Manchester and
Swansea, see overleaf.**

Note that, as well as attending these concerts,
you can also join in the Last Night at the BBC
Big Screens in Birmingham (Chamberlain Square),
Hull (Victoria Square), Liverpool (Clayton Square)
and Manchester (Exchange Square).

Advance Booking from 16 May • General Booking from 13 June: 020 7589 8212
Online booking bbc.co.uk/proms

PROMS IN THE PARK
Donegall Square, Belfast

Noel Thompson *presenter*
Gerry Anderson *presenter*

Ulster Orchestra

As Proms in the Park comes to Northern Ireland for the fourth year running, the Ulster Orchestra is back once again in the grounds of Belfast's City Hall to play its part in this year's festive open-air celebrations. The evening will be hosted by the BBC's Belfast-born Northern Ireland news anchorman Noel Thompson, with Radio Foyle's own Gerry Anderson mingling among the crowd.

Noel Thompson

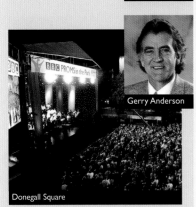
Gerry Anderson

Donegall Square

A limited number of free tickets are available by calling 0870 333 1918, textphone 08000 153350, or visiting bbc.co.uk/ni/tickets. Or write to: BBC Northern Ireland Ticket Unit (Proms), Broadcasting House, Ormeau Avenue, Belfast BT2 8HQ

PROMS IN THE PARK
Glasgow Green

BBC Scottish Symphony Orchestra
John Wilson *conductor*

BBC Proms in the Park goes north of the border for the third year running, with the BBC's own Scottish orchestra once again taking centre-stage.

Glasgow Green

Admission by free ticket only.
Tickets available from 1 July by calling 08700 100900 or visiting bbc.co.uk/proms

PROMS IN THE PARK
Heaton Park, Manchester

Heather Stott *presenter*

BBC Philharmonic

BBC Proms in the Park return to Manchester with another evening of thrilling live music-making from the BBC's local orchestra, the fabulous Philharmonic.

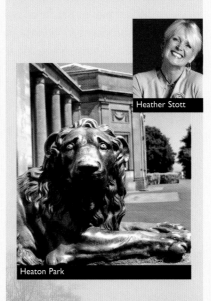
Heather Stott

Heaton Park

Tickets: £10.00 (under-12s free with an accompanying adult), available now from the Library Theatre box office (0161 236 7110) or online at bbc.co.uk/proms

PROMS IN THE PARK
Singleton Park, Swansea

Aled Jones *presenter*
Katherine Jenkins *mezzo-soprano*

BBC National Orchestra of Wales

Proms in the Park returns to Swansea's Singleton Park for a concert presented by Aled Jones, former child star and more recent *Strictly Come Dancing* contestant, and featuring current Welsh singing sensation Katherine Jenkins, the former schoolteacher from Neath who last year, aged only 23, signed the biggest classical recording deal in UK history and became the fastest-selling female opera singer since Maria Callas.

Katherine Jenkins

Aled Jones

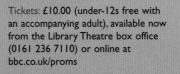
Singleton Park

Tickets: available from the BBC Call NOW Line on 08700 13 1812 and in person or by phone from the Grand Theatre, Singleton Street, Swansea (01792 475715).

BBC Family Prom in the Park:
Around the World in 80 Minutes with *Blue Peter*

Konnie Huq

Matt Baker

Blue Peter presenters Konnie Huq and Matt Baker take us on a worldwide musical journey in celebration of the centenary of French author Jules Verne and his immortal fantasy *Around the World in 80 Days*. On stage will be the BBC Concert Orchestra, along with artists from around the world, plus spectacular footage on the big screens to set the scene. And we'll be joined in Hyde Park by a surprise VIP, the biggest guest we have ever seen. So whether you're travelling by bike, bus, train or car – or even hot-air balloon – get globe-trotting along to Hyde Park on Sunday 11 September for an amazing cross-cultural, boundary-busting afternoon of world music and musical fun.

BBC FAMILY PROM IN THE PARK
Hyde Park, London

Around the World in 80 Minutes with Blue Peter

THE ROYAL PARKS

Konnie Huq *presenter*
Matt Baker *presenter*

BBC Concert Orchestra
Artists from around the world

The Hyde Park festivities don't end with the Last Night. So why not take the kids along for a fun-filled family afternoon as *Blue Peter*'s Konnie Huq and Matt Baker are joined by the BBC Concert Orchestra and a host of celebrity friends to celebrate the centenary of French sci-fi writer Jules Verne by taking you around the world of music in just 80 minutes – 115,200 times faster than the challenge that Verne set his heroes, Phileas Fogg and his manservant Passepartout.

Gates open 3.30pm.
Entertainment on stage from 4.30pm.

Event sponsored by
Lloyds TSB

Tickets: £14.00 adults, £9.00 children 3–16 (under-3s free), available now by post/fax using the Booking Form (*facing page 142*), by phone on 0870 899 8001 (24 hours, national rate) or online at bbc.co.uk/proms, and also (after 13 June) from the Royal Albert Hall on 020 7589 8212 (9.00am–9.00pm). *A £2.25 transaction fee applies.*

Tickets can also be bought in person (no transaction fee) from the BBC Shops at 50 Margaret Street, London W1 and Bush House, Strand, London WC2.

BBC
FAMILY
PROM
in the Park

MONDAYS AT 1.00PM
now at Cadogan Hall
5 Sloane Terrace, London SW1
(see map, page 135)

*Broadcast live on BBC Radio 3 and repeated
the following Saturday at 12.00 noon*

PROMS
CHAMBER MUSIC

Proms Chamber Music is on the move
to a larger venue. What better way to
celebrate its 10th season than by being
able to welcome an even bigger audience?

Chamber music is about to get bigger! After a sell-out run of some years at the Victoria & Albert Museum, the Proms Monday-lunchtime chamber music series celebrates its 10th season by setting sail for more spacious moorings at the newly-opened Cadogan Hall, just off Sloane Square.

The first season, back in 1996, took place at the Royal College of Music, and the aim, then as now, was to resonate with the main Proms series through chamber works that pick up on Proms themes, artists and anniversaries.

The first concert also included a UK premiere: a new string quartet by Elliott Carter, who was himself present to accept the award of the gold medal of the Royal Philharmonic Society. Since then, new music has remained central to Proms Chamber Music, with premieres of significant works commissioned from Martin Butler, John Casken, Joe Duddell, Simon Holt, Joseph Phibbs, Steven Stucky, Judith Weir and John Woolrich. Weir's eloquent song-cycle *The Voice of Desire*, premiered during the 2003 series by the mezzo-soprano Alice Coote and the pianist Julius Drake – the artists for whom it was written – went on to win her a British Academy of Composers award.

Proms Chamber Music has been at the V&A, in the elegant Lecture Theatre, since

LEFT & ABOVE
Cadogan Hall (as seen from Sedding Street) and a detail from one of the stained-glass windows designed by Arild Rosenkrantz

Every Prom live on BBC Radio 3 and bbc.co.uk/proms
Advance Booking from 16 May • General Booking from 13 June: 020 7589 8212

BOTTOM & RIGHT
Inside Cadogan Hall,
the new home for
Proms Chamber Music

BELOW
Stephanie Hughes: presenter
of Proms Chamber Music

its second season, enjoying a fruitful intermingling of the worlds of music and the fine arts. But while the success of the concerts has grown, the number of seats available has remained limited – 300 at a squeeze! So the arrival on the scene of a brand-new concert hall nearby, seating 900 and perfect for chamber music, has pointed the way towards an exciting future.

Cadogan Hall is also a work of art in its own right. Completed in 1907 as a Christian Science church, it was designed by Robert Fellowes Chisholm, who had been the British Government's consultant architect in India. Chisholm filled the Hall with a dramatic mixture of Byzantine, Romanesque and Indo-Saracenic elements. In addition, a Danish nobleman, Baron von Rosenkrantz, who was a designer for Tiffany in New York, devised stained glass throughout the building as variations on a Celtic knot theme.

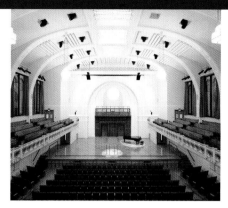

After a decade or so of neglect, Cadogan Hall is now restored to its original glory, and the refurbishment has also enhanced its rich acoustic. It is already establishing itself as a valuable addition to the London concert scene. So do come and hear for yourself – as you can see from the listings overleaf, there's a great line-up of Proms Chamber Music concerts waiting for you this summer!

Edward Blakeman
Editor, Live Music, BBC Radio 3

How to Book

£8.00 ADVANCE TICKETS
Advance Booking, from Monday 16 May
To book £8.00 tickets during the Advance Booking period, use the Booking Form *(facing page 142)* or the Online Ticket Request system (at bbc.co.uk/proms)

General Booking, from Monday 13 June
Once General Booking has opened, you can also book £8.00 tickets by telephone or in person at the Royal Albert Hall (on 020 7589 8212) or Cadogan Hall (on 020 7730 4500), as well as online.

On the day
£8.00 tickets (if still available) can only be bought at Cadogan Hall, from 10.00am.

£4.00 GALLERY DAY TICKETS
On the day
At least 150 Gallery (bench) seats will be available for just £4.00 each on the day of the concert. These tickets can only be bought at Cadogan Hall, from 10.00am. They must be purchased in person and with cash only, and are limited to two tickets per transaction.

£20.00 PCM SERIES PASS
Hear all eight concerts for just £20.00, with guaranteed entrance to the Gallery until 12.50pm (after which PCM Pass-holders may be asked to join the day queue).

Advance Booking, from Monday 16 May
During the Advance Booking period, PCM Series Passes can be purchased using the Booking Form *(facing page 142)* or the Online Ticket Request system (at bbc.co.uk/proms).

General Booking, from Monday 13 June
Once General Booking has opened, PCM Series Passes can also be purchased by telephone or in person at the Royal Albert Hall (on 020 7589 8212) as well as online.
PCM Passes are subject to availability.

Doors will open at 11.45am and entrance to the auditorium will be from 12.30pm.

The Adverb

Mondays, 2.15pm
Cadogan Hall
(immediately after Proms Chamber Music concerts)

Admission free to Proms Chamber Music ticket-holders
Recorded for broadcast on BBC Radio 3 as a series of interval features during the evening Proms

Ian McMillan

Ian McMillan, from Radio 3's language and literature show *The Verb*, and guest presenters, writers and actors, give a series of literary performances inspired by this season's Proms themes of 'The Sea' and 'Fairy Tales'. Enjoy readings of classic poetry and prose from across the centuries and new work commissioned specially for the series.

PCM 1

1.00pm – c2.00pm

PCM 2

1.00pm – c2.00pm

PCM 3

1.00pm – c2.00pm

PCM 4

1.00pm – c2.00pm

Fauré
L'horizon chimérique   8'

Barber
Dover Beach   9'

Warlock
Songs, including 'Ha'nacker Mill';
'The Night'; 'My Own Country'   15'

And a selection of traditional
sea-songs, including 'Tom Bowling'
and 'Trade Winds'

Sir Thomas Allen baritone
Imogen Cooper piano
Royal String Quartet

Sir Thomas Allen

The star of last year's
Last Night launches
the 10th anniversary
season of lunchtime
concerts in the
company of a
distinguished pianist
and a young quartet
from BBC Radio 3's
New Generation
Artists. Alongside a tribute to Peter
Warlock – one of England's greatest songwriters, who died 75 years ago – is an
exploration of aspects of the Proms
theme of the sea, from Barber's and
Fauré's visions of its immensity and
mystery, to more salty celebrations of
seafaring life through the centuries.

📖 'The Sea', pages 4–13

Messiaen
Theme and Variations   10'

Ravel
Violin Sonata   25'

John Adams
Road Movies   16'

Leila Josefowicz violin
John Novacek piano

As a curtain-raiser to our 'Violins!!' day
(Proms 20–22), an imaginative recital from
a brilliant young violinist who also plays
the Bruch concerto this season (Prom
11). Ravel's unconventional, jazz-inflected
sonata is framed by Messiaen's wedding
gift to his first wife, and Adams's
delightfully 'relaxed drive down a not
unfamiliar road'.

Leila Josefowicz

Lutoslawski
Chain 1
                                            10'

John Woolrich
After the Clock   15'
BBC commission: world premiere

Copland
Appalachian Spring – suite   23'

National Youth Orchestra Sinfonietta
Paul Watkins conductor

A Proms debut for this elite ensemble
made up of principal players from the
National Youth Orchestra of Great Britain,
appearing at the Proms next Saturday
(Prom 31). Lutoslawski's capricious
soundscape of overlapping ideas contrasts
with the radiant wide-open spaces of
Copland's ballet score in its original
version for 13 players. John Woolrich's
fascinating new piece has echoes of the
darkly comic world of Goya's paintings.

Appalachian Spring: the original ballet

📖 'New Music', pages 50–57

Duparc
La vie antérieure; Chanson triste;
Phidylé   12'

Chausson
Les papillons; Le colibri; Le temps
de lilas; Chanson perpétuelle   15'

Hahn
Infidélité; Rêverie; Si mes vers avaient
des ailes; Y'a des arbres   10'

Satie
La diva de l'Empire; Je te veux   7'

Dame Felicity Lott soprano
Pascal Rogé piano

'Endless song': the title of anniversary
composer Ernest Chausson's nostalgically
passionate *mélodie* sums up a style and
a moment of intense lyrical beauty in
French music at the end of the 19th
century. All that is captured in this recital
by a much-loved singer who has made this
repertoire her own.

Dame Felicity Lott

📀 **2.15pm The Adverb** (CH)
See page 115

📀 **2.15pm The Adverb** (CH)
See page 115

📀 **2.15pm The Adverb** (CH)
See page 115

📀 **2.15pm The Adverb** (CH)
See page 115

| MONDAY 15 AUGUST | MONDAY 22 AUGUST | MONDAY 29 AUGUST | MONDAY 5 SEPTEMBER |

PCM 5
1.00pm – c2.00pm

Brahms
Intermezzo in E flat major,
Op. 117 No.1   4'

Tatjana Komarova
Tänze mit verbundenen Augen   10'
UK premiere

Schubert
Piano Sonata in B flat major,
D960   40'

Lars Vogt *piano*

Lars Vogt

After playing the Grieg concerto (Prom 38), this celebrated pianist gives the UK premiere of a solo work by his composer wife. 'Blindfold Dances' portrays the searching, questioning spirit of mankind in music both restless and mercurial. It complements Brahms's wistful lullaby and Schubert's compassionate and life-affirming final sonata.

📖 'New Music', pages 50–57

💬 **2.15pm The Adverb** (CH)
See page 115

PCM 6
1.00pm – c2.00pm

Tippett
The Heart's Assurance   18'

Purcell, arr. Tippett and Bergmann
Sweeter than Roses; I Attempt from Love's Sickness to Fly;
An Evening Hymn   9'

Tippett
Piano Sonata No. 3   24'

Andrew Kennedy *tenor*
Paul Crossley *piano*

The distinctive genius of Michael Tippett shines brightly in his moving song-cycle and exhilarating piano sonata – both creating an utterly personal sound-world. Tippett's centenary and his love of Purcell's music are celebrated by a young tenor from BBC Radio 3's New Generation Artists, and a renowned pianist who knew Tippett well and is the dedicatee of the Third Sonata.

Paul Crossley

📖 'Anniversary Composers', pages 36–38

💬 **2.15pm The Adverb** (CH)
See page 115

PCM 7
1.00pm – c2.00pm

Monteverdi
Madrigals – Book 5 (selection)   10'

Carissimi
Jonah   18'

With motets by Carissimi and instrumental works of the period

I Fagiolini
Robert Hollingworth *director*

I Fagiolini

This lively vocal and instrumental ensemble celebrates 1605 – a vintage year for Italian music. It saw the birth in Rome of Carissimi, now credited as the inventor of the oratorio. *Jonah* is one of his most famous – full of glorious music, and an absolute whale of a tale! Meanwhile, in Mantua in 1605, Monteverdi was at the peak of his powers, producing his impassioned fifth book of madrigals.

📖 'Anniversary Composers', page 42

💬 **2.15pm The Adverb** (CH)
See page 115

PCM 8
1.00pm – c2.00pm

Haydn
String Quartet in F minor,
Op. 20 No. 5   22'

Bartók
String Quartet No. 2   28'

Artemis Quartet

A homage to Bartók on the 60th anniversary of his death, with a vigorous and hauntingly beautiful work, played by a superb young quartet from BBC Radio 3's New Generation Artists. It is matched with one of Haydn's so-called 'Sun Quartets' – a product of the high summer of his career, full of emotional intensity and ultimate high spirits. 'The end – praise be to God!' he wrote on the final page.

Bartók

💬 **2.15pm The Adverb** (CH)
See page 115

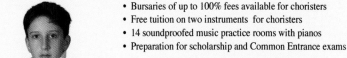

BBC Symphony Chorus

Stephen Jackson Director

The BBC Symphony Chorus is one of the finest and most distinctive amateur choirs in the country and performs a wide range of challenging repertoire. Recent highlights include premieres by John Cage, Judith Bingham and Mark-Anthony Turnage, John Adams's *Harmonium* conducted by the composer and two works by James MacMillan as part of the BBC Symphony Orchestra's January Composer Weekend.

As resident chorus at the BBC Proms, this year the BBC Symphony Chorus's performances include the Requiems by Brahms and Verdi, Mahler's *Das klagende Lied* and, in Tippett's centenary year, his *Vision of St. Augustine*, one of the most challenging works in the choral repertory.

> **"The BBC Symphony Chorus crackled with vigour and crisp enunciation."**
> The Times

> **"...complex polyphony beautifully negotiated by the BBC Symphony Chorus."**
> The Guardian

> **"...fabulously precise..."**
> Financial Times

> **"The BBC Symphony Chorus is a group of amateur singers who could put many professional radio choirs to shame."**
> Le Monde

2005-06 Season Highlights

During the BBC Symphony Orchestra's Barbican season, the BBC Symphony Chorus will perform:

Stravinsky *Symphony of Psalms*, conducted by Jiří Bělohlávek
Ravel *Daphnis & Chloë*, conducted by Pierre Boulez
Messiaen *Trois petites liturgies* and **Duruflé** Requiem, conducted by Donald Runnicles
Mozart Mass in C minor, conducted by David Robertson
Richard Rodney Bennett world premiere of a BBC commission, conducted by Martyn Brabbins

Would you like to join us?

The BBC Symphony Chorus is always interested in hearing from potential new members. If you would enjoy making music at the highest level with great conductors, orchestras and soloists, then this is the choir for you.

To apply or to find out more, visit www.bbc.co.uk/symphonychorus
Or contact: The Administrator, BBC Symphony Chorus, BBC Maida Vale Studios, Delaware Road, London W9 2LG
Tel: 020 7765 4715

BBC RADIO 3
90-93 FM

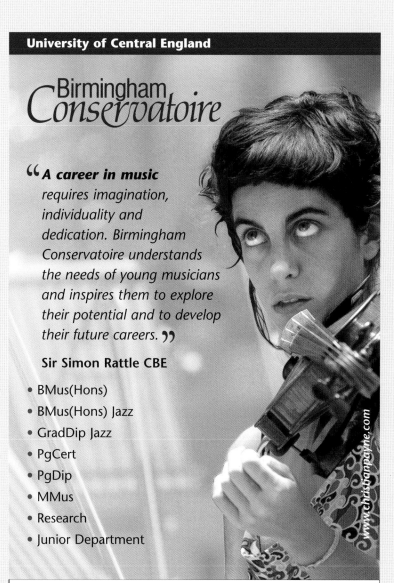

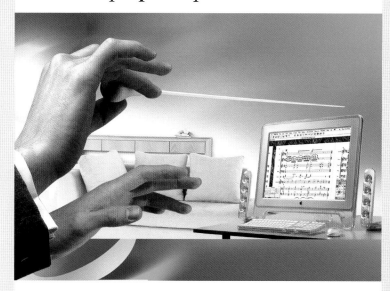

THE PROMS – WITHIN EVERYONE'S REACH

The BBC: bringing the **Proms** to you
– in concert, on radio, television,
online and now on your mobile phone
bbc.co.uk/proms

**Listening to the Proms on
DAB Digital Radio and Digital TV
(Satellite, Cable and Freeview)**

Not only can you listen to every Prom
in digital sound via BBC Radio 3
but you can also receive 'now playing'
information and notes about the music while
you listen (*on DAB Radio and Freeview only*)

**Watching the Proms on Digital TV
(Satellite, Cable and Freeview)**

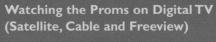

Not only can you watch the best of the Proms
season in both live and deferred relays on BBC1,
BBC2 and BBC4
but you can also access specially-written
programme notes or synchronised captions by
pressing red on your digital remote. Plus, on the
Last Night, press red to see the notes and choose
a Proms in the Park concert from around the UK

Interacting with the Proms on the Internet

Not only can you get full concert information on the BBC Proms website at bbc.co.uk/proms **but you can also** book tickets online via the Royal Albert Hall website

Not only can you listen live to every Prom via the website **but you can also** listen on demand to most Proms for seven days after broadcast

Not only can you take part in a wide range of Proms debates on our messageboard **but you could also** win tickets by sending in your reviews of Proms concerts

Keeping in touch with the Proms on your mobile phone

Not only can you sign up for free daily text updates during the Proms season (text PROMS CLUB to 83111*) **but you can also** access full Proms listings and broadcast information at any time via the Proms mobile site at bbc.co.uk/mobile**.

*You will be charged your usual text rates for registration to the service. Each message you receive will be free to you.
To unsubscribe at any time text STOP to 83111.
Full terms and conditions available on the Proms website – bbc.co.uk/proms
**WAP-enabled phones only

BBC MUSIC INTRO

Scheme sponsored by

Lloyds TSB

Introducing families to great music for only £4 a seat!

In this digital mass-media age the BBC is energetically maintaining its long tradition of finding fresh and innovative ways of encouraging new audiences to experience the thrill of live classical music.

In Manchester, Scotland, Wales and London, the resident BBC orchestras all run active learning programmes that are forging ever stronger links with local schools and communities. The Proms Out + About scheme exists to take BBC orchestras out into the diverse communities of London: so far it has taken the BBC Symphony Orchestra to Brixton and the BBC Concert Orchestra to Hackney, and has brought over 700 new families to the Royal Albert Hall.

Now the 2005 Proms season sees the launch of BBC Music Intro, a major new ticket scheme – sponsored by Lloyds TSB, and featuring all five of the BBC orchestras – that aims to make the first experience of going to a classical music concert more affordable and accessible for young people and their families all over the country. Over the next two years, as well as opportunities to attend more than a dozen BBC Proms concerts, each of the BBC orchestras will be offering tickets for four concerts per season at only **£4** for young people (aged between 5 and 16) and their families.

As well as offering the opportunity to experience some of the finest music-making in the world, each Music Intro ticket includes a free pre-concert workshop in which professional musicians and workshop leaders will present lively, interactive introductions to the concert programme and set the scene for the night ahead.

A selection of Proms featuring world premieres, classic symphonies and a colourful cross-section of the season's themes and anniversaries will be available as part of the scheme this year, together with opportunities to attend both the Blue Peter Proms and our 'Violins!!' day – one of this season's flagship youth events.

For more information, visit the Proms website:
bbc.co.uk/proms

PROMS EXTRAS

Modum Louthers (Musgrave); Hans Jorg Michel/Boosey & Hawkes (Glanert); Marianne Grøndahl/Chester Novello (Abrahamsen); Gérard Billaudot Éditeur (Dalbavie)

In the Royal Albert Hall.

Admission is free. Tickets can be collected from Door 6 at the Royal Albert Hall from half an hour beforehand. Latecomers will not be admitted until a suitable break in the performance.

Each Composer Portrait will be recorded for broadcast on BBC Radio 3 later the same day, immediately following the main evening Prom.

Proms Composer Portraits

Proms Composer Portraits feature music for chamber ensemble by four distinguished composers who all have major new orchestral works being performed at the Proms this season, including two BBC commissions. This year, for the first time, Proms Composer Portraits will take place in the Arena of the Royal Albert Hall.

During these early-evening events, the composers, in conversation with BBC Radio 3's Andrew McGregor, will discuss their works being heard in the main evening Prom, as well as presenting a different aspect of their creative activities through smaller-scale pieces performed by young musicians from leading music colleges and conservatoires around the UK. The series opens with Scottish composer Thea Musgrave and continues with Detlev Glanert from Germany, Hans Abrahamsen from Denmark and Marc-André Dalbavie from France.

Thea Musgrave
Wednesday 20 July, 5.15pm
(before Prom 6)
Impromptu No. 1, for flute and oboe; In the Still of the Night, for solo viola; Serenade, for flute, clarinet, viola, cello and harp
Contemporary Consort of the Royal College of Music

Detlev Glanert
Tuesday 26 July, 5.30pm
(before Prom 15)
Violin Sonata; Four Fantasies, for solo piano – Nos. 3 and 4; Serenade, for cello and piano
Musicians from Trinity College of Music

Hans Abrahamsen
Monday 1 August, 5.30pm
(before Prom 24)
Hymn, for solo cello; Storm and Still, for solo cello; Capriccio Bagatels, for solo violin; String Quartet No. 2
Musicians from the Royal Northern College of Music

Marc-André Dalbavie
Tuesday 16 August, 5.30pm
(before Prom 43)
Trio, for violin, horn and piano; Palimpseste, for flute, clarinet, violin, viola, cello and piano
Musicians from the Guildhall School of Music & Drama

Proms Question Time

Who Pays for New Music?
Thursday 21 July, c9.50pm (after Prom 8)
Royal Albert Hall, West Arena Foyer
Admission free to ticket-holders for Prom 8 (subject to capacity)

Following the London premiere of James MacMillan's *A Scotch Bestiary*, a distinguished panel debates the issue of financing musical creativity.

Chairman **Christopher Cook** puts questions to

Roger Wright, Controller of BBC Radio 3, **Kathryn McDowell**, Director of the City of London Festival and Managing Director designate of the London Symphony Orchestra, and composer **Joby Talbot**, whose BBC commission *Sneaker Wave* was premiered at last year's Proms.

To find out more, including how you can submit questions and comments, please visit bbc.co.uk/proms

BBC Proms/Guardian Young Composers Concert
Thursday 28 July, 4.00pm at Cadogan Hall. Recorded for broadcast on BBC Radio 3 on 2 August

Hear music by some of the UK's most talented young composers in a concert featuring winning pieces from the seventh BBC Proms/Guardian Young Composers Competition, judged by composers Colin Matthews, Fraser Trainer and Tansy Davies, conductor Martyn Brabbins, Andrew Kurowski from BBC Radio 3 and *Guardian* journalist Peter Kingston.

To attend this free invitation concert, call the BBC Proms on 020 7765 5575 or email proms@bbc.co.uk

THE ENCORE
*Sunday 21 August, c8.45pm (after Prom 50)
Royal Albert Hall, West Arena Foyer*

Iain Burnside in conversation with musicians of the BBC SO and their new Chief Conductor Designate Jiří Bělohlávek.

Proms Films

Back in the 1890s, the first Proms audiences at the old Queen's Hall were entertained with interval showings of such pioneering silent films (or 'Animated Photographs') as 'Incoming Tide at Worthing', 'The Sleeping Coachman' and 'Feeding the Pelicans in the Park'. This year, movies finally return to the Proms with a season of films more directly inspired by the music and themes of the season.

Sunday afternoons at the Royal Geographical Society, Kensington Gore.

Admission free and unticketed; doors open half an hour before start-time.

Sunday 17 July, 2.30pm
A Midsummer Night's Dream (116 mins, certificate PG)
Michael Hoffman's 1999 adaptation of Shakespeare's forest fairy-tale. With a cast including Rupert Everett, Michelle Pfeiffer, Stanley Tucci, Kevin Kline, Calista Flockhart and Anna Friel.

Sunday 31 July, 2.30pm
The Red Violin (131 mins, certificate 15)
With music by John Corigliano (performed by violinist Joshua Bell), François Girard's 1998 film stars Samuel L. Jackson as a collector whose efforts to discover the secrets of the famous 'Red Violin' carry us through centuries and across continents to Cremona, Vienna, Oxford and China.

Sunday 14 August, 3.00pm
Eroica (85 mins, certificate TBC)
Simon Cellan Jones's acclaimed BBC television film charts the real-time unveiling of a piece of music that was to change the course of cultural history: Beethoven's Third Symphony (conducted on the soundtrack by Sir John Eliot Gardiner).

Sunday 21 August, 3.00pm
Holocaust: A Music Memorial Film from Auschwitz (90 mins, certificate TBC)
James Kent's film, made to mark the 60th anniversary of the liberation of Auschwitz and dedicated to the memory of those murdered in the Nazi genocide, features memories of Holocaust survivors interspersed with musical performances, filmed in Auschwitz itself, from Maxim Vengerov, Emanuel Ax and others. Introduced by cellist and Holocaust survivor Anita Lasker-Wallfisch.

Pre-Prom Talks & Events

Venue codes:
RAH • Auditorium, Royal Albert Hall   RGS • Royal Geographical Society
Admission is free to ticket-holders for the following Prom.

Friday 15 July, 5.30pm RGS
Tippett biographer Ian Kemp introduces *A Child of Our Time*.

Saturday 16 July, 6.00pm RAH
Writer and broadcaster Roderick Swanston talks about the work of Gilbert & Sullivan.

Sunday 17 July, 5.00pm RAH
Conductor Paul McCreesh in conversation with Nicholas Kenyon, Director of the Proms.

Tuesday 19 July, 5.30pm RGS
Michael Berkeley discusses his *Concerto for Orchestra* with Richard Hickox and Tommy Pearson.

Monday 25 July, 5.30pm RAH
John Butt, Professor of Music at Glasgow University, on Tippett's *Vision of St Augustine*.

Thursday 28 July, 6.00pm RAH
Composer John Corigliano and conductor Marin Alsop talk to Sarah Walker.

Tuesday 2 August, 5.30pm RGS
Members of the Philharmonia Baroque Orchestra and conductor Nicholas McGegan introduce and demonstrate their instruments, with Lindsay Kemp.

Wednesday 3 August, 5.45pm RAH
Introduction to Indian classical instruments with musicians from the Bhavan Centre and Stephanie Hughes.

Thursday 4 August, 5.30pm RGS
Huw Watkins discusses his new work with Anthony Burton and soloists Philip Dukes and Josephine Knight.

Monday 8 August, 6.00pm RAH
'Is it a Planet?': composer Colin Matthews and astronomer Heather Couper with Tommy Pearson.

Tuesday 9 August, 6.00pm RAH
Violinist Philippe Graffin discusses Coleridge-Taylor's concerto with Mark Lowther.

Wednesday 10 August, 6.00pm RAH
Unsuk Chin discusses her *snagS & Snarls* with Gillian Moore.

Thursday 11 August, 6.00pm RAH
Piers Burton-Page on the life and works of Karl Amadeus Hartmann.

Friday 12 August, 6.00pm RGS
Composer Bent Sørensen in conversation with Stephen Johnson.

Monday 15 August, 6.00pm RAH
Donald Nally, WNO chorus-master, on Tchaikovsky's fairy-tale opera *Iolanta*.

Thursday 18 August, 6.00pm RAH
Richard Wigley talks to musicians from the New Zealand Symphony Orchestra and their Chief Executive, Peter Walls.

Saturday 20 August, 6.00pm RAH
Russian composer Sofia Gubaidulina talks to Barrie Gavin.

Tuesday 23 August, 4.30pm RAH
Donald Burrows on Handel's *Julius Caesar*.

Thursday 25 August, 6.00pm RAH
Morgan Hayes talks to Andrew Kurowski.

Friday 26 August, 6.00pm RAH
John Deathridge on Liszt's *A Faust Symphony*.

Saturday 3 September, 5.30pm RAH
Working together: the Principal of the Royal Academy of Music and the President of the Juilliard School talk to Sandy Burnett.

Sunday 4 September, 5.00pm RAH
Antony Beaumont on Zemlinsky's Andersen-inspired *Die Seejungfrau* (The Little Mermaid).

Monday 5 September, 5.15pm RAH
Audience Forum: put your questions to Nicholas Kenyon, Director of the Proms, and David Elliott, Chief Executive of the Royal Albert Hall.

Friday 9 September, 6.00pm RAH
Mark-Anthony Turnage talks to Tom Service.

Ronald Grant Archive ('Midsummer Night's Dream'; 'Red Violin'); BBC

Proms Quiz

Monday 18 July, c8.10pm (during the long interval
of *Die Walküre*, Prom 4)
Royal Albert Hall, West Arena Foyer
*Admission free to ticket-holders for Prom 4 (subject
to capacity).*
*Recorded for broadcast on BBC Radio 3 during
the interval of Prom 8 on Thursday 21 July.*

BBC Radio 3's Stephanie Hughes hosts the first ever
Proms Quiz with a panel made up of broadcaster
Sir David Attenborough, composer Judith Bingham,
CBSO Chief Executive Stephen Maddock and
conductor Jane Glover.

Submit your Proms questions via the website
at bbc.co.uk/proms or by post to: Proms Quiz, Room 330,
Henry Wood House, 3–6 Langham Place, London W1B 3DF.
Two questions will be selected from all those submitted.
The winners will each receive two complimentary tickets
for Prom 4 and have the opportunity of putting their
question in person to the panel on the night.

Out + About

Once again the BBC Proms are going Out + About
– taking the live concert experience to a London
local community and introducing live orchestral
music to people who might not have been to a
concert or ever heard an orchestra before. Over
the last two years the BBC Symphony Orchestra
has been to the Brixton Academy in south London
and Hammersmith Town Hall in west London, while
the BBC Concert Orchestra has performed at the
Hackney Empire in east London. This year, on
Wednesday 15 June, the BBC Symphony Orchestra,
with members of Islington Music Centre and other
young musicians from the surrounding area, will
once again be welcoming a family audience and
helping them to discover what an orchestra is and
how it works through music that travels the seas
and weaves in and out of fantasy and fairy tales.
For further details call 020 7765 5575
or see the Proms website at bbc.co.uk/proms

 90-93 FM

Proms on BBC Radio 3

Every Prom is broadcast live on BBC
Radio 3* and many can be heard again
on weekday afternoons, usually at 2.00pm.

Proms Chamber Music concerts
are broadcast live and repeated
the following Saturday at 12.00 noon.

Proms Composer Portraits (see page 125)
are broadcast the same day immediately
after the main evening Prom.

Twenty Minutes talks and features are
broadcast in the intervals of the evening
Proms and many reflect Proms themes
and anniversaries. This year they include
the very first *Proms Quiz* (see *left*),
plus two special series: *Talking Proms*,
a magazine programme broadcast live
from the Royal Albert Hall during each
Friday night's Prom; and *The Adverb*,
literary performances inspired by the
Proms themes of the sea and fairy tales,
recorded at 2.15pm after each Proms
Chamber Music concert (see *page 115*).

In Tune (weekdays, 5.00pm to start of
evening Prom) features interviews,
performances and news surrounding
the Proms season.

Morning on 3 (weekdays, 7.00–10.00am;
weekends, 7.00–9.00am) presents music
and updates on the season.

Summer CD Review
(Saturdays, 9.00am–12.00 noon)
reflects repertoire related to the Proms,
and explores eight specific works in the
Building a Library feature (9.30am).

Listen out too for the following special Proms-related programming:

Proms Preview Evening
(Monday 11 July, 7.30–10.30pm)
Musical highlights and the inside story
on the coming season.

Proms Sunday Features

Sunday 31 July, 9.30pm
In Search of Hans Christian Andersen
Michael Rosen and Lars Tharp make
personal journeys to reveal the man,
his life, and the widely differing legacies
he left in his homeland and abroad.

Sunday 7 August, 7.15pm
Silence, Exile and Cunning
What should a German artist do under
the Nazis? Piers Burton-Page explores
Karl Amadeus Hartmann's decision to
go into 'inner exile'.

Sunday 14 August, 9.30pm
A Man of All Time
Tom Service traces the course of Michael
Tippett's life and music in the composer's
own words, taken from interviews
preserved in the BBC Archives.

All times subject to change

*except for the Blue Peter Proms, which are
recorded for later broadcast*

All broadcast details were correct at the time of going to press.
For current schedules, consult *Radio Times* or other listings
publications, or visit the Proms website at bbc.co.uk/proms

Proms on BBC World Service

Details on bbc.co.uk/worldservice

BBC Proms 2005 Guide

Published by BBC Proms Publications.
Editorial Office: Room 330,
Henry Wood House, 3–6 Langham Place,
London W1B 3DF

Distributed by BBC Worldwide,
80 Wood Lane, London W12 0TT

Editor Mark Pappenheim
Publications Manager Sarah Breeden
Editorial Manager Edward Bhesania
Publications Officer Tania Conrad
Publications Assistant Mary Galloway

Design Premm Design Ltd, London
Cover photograph (RAH) Simon Keats
Advertising Cabbell Publishing Ltd, London
Printed by Taylor Bloxham Ltd, Leicester

© BBC 2005
ISBN 0-563-52271-2

BBC Proms 2005

Director Nicholas Kenyon CBE,
Controller, BBC Proms, Live Events
and TV Classical Music
Personal Assistant Yvette Pusey

Artistic Administrator Rosemary Gent
Concerts Administrator
Helen Burridge
Concerts Assistants Isabella Kernot,
Tom Nelson

Marketing Manager Kate Finch
Publicist Victoria Bevan
Assistant Publicist Leanne Williams
**Marketing and Audience
Development Officer** Doug Buist
Marketing & Publicity Assistant
Jacqui Garbett

Business & Finance Manager David Stott
Management Assistant Tricia Twigg

Editor, Live Music, BBC Radio 3
Edward Blakeman
Editor, TV Classical Music
Oliver Macfarlane

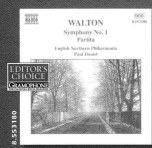

1605
Treason & Dischord
William Byrd and The Gunpowder Plot
performed by The King's Singers & Concordia

Relive one of the most stupendous acts of treason in English history, as an extraordinary collaboration between leading international artists The King's Singers and English viol consort, Concordia, marks the 400th anniversary year of the thwarting of the Gunpowder Plot. A nationwide concert tour in Cathedrals and historic houses associated with the Plot will echo to the haunting music of this worrying, but enterprising time.

The music, structured around Byrd's perfect 4–part Mass contains motets by catholic composers, protestant anthems celebrating the downfall of the plot, and a commission from British composer, Francis Pott, a commentary and comparison between the 17th Century 5/11 event and the 21st century world troubles.

What led Guy Fawkes and the Catholic conspirators of 1605 to set 36 barrels of gunpowder under Parliament, attempting to assassinate King James I, the nobles, bishops and the Commons, all in one fell swoop? The performance will recreate the atmosphere in the Jacobean court, the dangers of singing Mass in secret, the story of the conspiracy and its downfall.

Lichfield Cathedral
Saturday 18 June 2005
Box Office
Lichfield Tourist Information
01543 308209
Price £15
Concession £13.50

The Royal Shakespeare Theatre
Sunday 19 June 2005
Box Office
0870 609 1110
Price £20/£15
Concession £13.50

Worcester Cathedral
Wednesday 28 September 2005
Box Office
Huntingdon Arts, Huntingdon Hall
01905 611 427
Price £15
Concession £13.50

Alnwick Castle
Thursday 29 September 2005
Box Office
Alnwick Playhouse
01665 510 785
Price £15
Concession £13.50

York Minster
Friday 30 September 2005
Box Office
York Theatre Royal
01904 623 568
Price £20/£15
Concession £13.50

Final Gala Concert
Friday 5 November
Enquiries
0870 420 2326
Tickets from £15

All performances begin at 7.30pm

A Gala Banquet will take place on May 6 at the Tower of London.
For further information on corporate packages for all events, please contact
info@ptarmiganproductions.co.uk

ptarmigan productions™

www.ptarmiganproductions.co.uk

In support of The Prince's Trust

Prince's Trust

Registered Charity Number 1079675

HOW TO BOOK

ADVANCE BOOKING
By post, fax and online – opens Monday 16 May

Use the Advance Booking Form or visit bbc.co.uk/proms

To take advantage of the Advance Booking period – and enjoy your best chance of securing the seats you want – you must use the official Advance Booking Form (facing page 142) or the Online Ticket Request system on the Proms website.

Note that all postal, fax and online bookings received before Monday 16 May will be treated as if they had arrived on that date and that Express Bookings will then be handled first (for full details see page 141).

Postal address:
BBC Proms, Box Office, Royal Albert Hall, London SW7 2AP
Fax: 020 7581 9311
Online booking: bbc.co.uk/proms

GENERAL BOOKING
In person, by phone or online – opens Monday 13 June

The Box Office is located at Door 12 of the Royal Albert Hall and is open 9.00am–9.00pm daily. Note that no booking fee applies to tickets bought in person at the Hall.

Telephone: 020 7589 8212
Online booking: bbc.co.uk/proms

THE LAST NIGHT OF THE PROMS

Because of the high demand for tickets, special booking arrangements apply. For full details – and your chance to enter the Last Night Ballot (exclusive to readers of the *BBC Proms 2005 Guide*) – see page 139.

PROMMING ON THE DAY – Don't book, just turn up

Up to 1,400 standing places are available at each concert. Weekend Promming Passes and Season Tickets can be booked in advance: see pages 134 and 136. Additionally, over 500 Arena and Gallery tickets are always on sale at the door from an hour beforehand, so you can just turn up on the night.

FOR NEW-LOOK CONCERT LISTINGS, SEE PAGES 84–117

Every Prom live on BBC Radio 3 and bbc.co.uk/proms • Advance Booking from 16 May • General Booking from 13 June: 020 7589 8212

SPECIAL OFFERS

Same Day Savers

Book for more than one concert on the same day and save £4.00 on your ticket for each subsequent concert.

Note: offer applies to matinée, evening and late night performances in the Royal Albert Hall. Not valid for Arena, Gallery and Circle (Restricted View) price areas.

Under-16s

The Proms are a great way to discover live music, and we encourage anyone over 5 years old to attend. Tickets for Under-16s can be purchased at half-price in any seating area for all Proms except the Last Night (Prom 74).

Note that the Blue Peter Proms (Proms 10 & 12) are expressly designed to introduce young children to concert-going.

Group Bookings

Group booking rates apply to all Proms except the Last Night (Prom 74). Groups of 10 or more can claim a 10% discount on the price of Centre/Side Stalls or Front/Rear Circle tickets for all Proms in the A, B, D, E and G price bands, and a 5% discount for C band concerts.

For more information, call the Group Booking Information Line: 020 7838 3108.

Please note that group purchases cannot be made online during the General Booking period.

Weekend Promming Pass

Beat the queues at the weekend and save money! In addition to discounted tickets, the Weekend Promming Pass offers guaranteed access up to 10 minutes before start-time to the Arena or Gallery standing areas for all concerts in the Royal Albert Hall on Fridays, Saturdays and Sundays (excluding Proms 10, 12, 73 and 74). Passes can be purchased in advance, by post or fax (using the Advance Booking Form) or online, and (from Monday 13 June) by phone or in person at the Box Office up to 6.00pm on Friday nights (5.30pm on 15 July and 19 August). Prices vary for each weekend depending on the number of concerts.

Note that Weekend 2 excludes the Blue Peter Proms; Weekend 7 includes Bank Holiday Monday (29 August); and there is no pass covering Proms 73 and 74.

Passes are non-transferable and signature ID may be requested upon entry. Purchase of a Weekend Pass does not guarantee entry to the Last Night, but tickets may be counted towards the 'Six Concert Rule' (see page 139) in conjunction with further Passes or Day Ticket stubs.

Note that you may only purchase a maximum of four passes per weekend (subject to availability).

For whole/half season Season Tickets, see page 136.

Weekend Promming Pass prices		
Weekend 1	Proms 1–3	£10
Weekend 2	Proms 9, 11 & 13	£10
Weekend 3	Proms 19–23	£14
Weekend 4	Proms 30–33	£14
Weekend 5	Proms 38–41	£14
Weekend 6	Proms 47–50	£14
Weekend 7	Proms 56–59	£14
Weekend 8	Proms 65–67	£10

BBC/Barney Newman; BBC/Lara Platman

All offers are subject to availability. Offers and discounts may not be combined.

Every Prom live on BBC Radio 3 and bbc.co.uk/proms • Advance Booking from 16 May • General Booking from 13 June: 020 7589 8212

134

GETTING TO PROMS VENUES

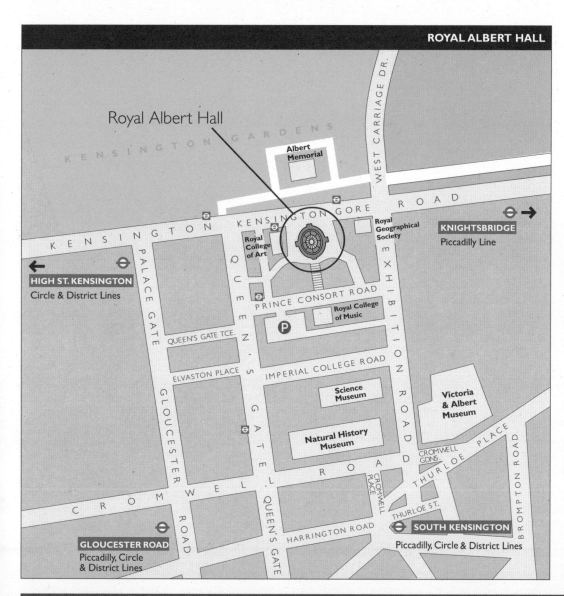

ROYAL ALBERT HALL

Royal Albert Hall

KENSINGTON GARDENS

Albert Memorial

WEST CARRIAGE DR.

KENSINGTON GORE ROAD

Royal College of Art

Royal Geographical Society

KNIGHTSBRIDGE
Piccadilly Line

HIGH ST. KENSINGTON
Circle & District Lines

KENSINGTON PALACE GATE

PRINCE CONSORT ROAD

QUEEN'S GATE TCE.

Royal College of Music

ELVASTON PLACE

QUEEN'S GATE

IMPERIAL COLLEGE ROAD

EXHIBITION ROAD

Science Museum

Victoria & Albert Museum

Natural History Museum

CROMWELL GDNS.

THURLOE PLACE

CROMWELL PLACE

BROMPTON ROAD

GLOUCESTER ROAD
Piccadilly, Circle & District Lines

CROMWELL ROAD

GLOUCESTER ROAD

THURLOE ST.

HARRINGTON ROAD

SOUTH KENSINGTON
Piccadilly, Circle & District Lines

The following buses service the Royal Albert Hall (via Kensington Gore, Queen's Gate and/or Prince Consort Road):
Nos. 9/N9, 10/N10, 52/N52, 70, 360

The following buses service Cadogan Hall (via Sloane Street and/or Sloane Square):
Nos. 11/N11, 19/N19, 22/N22, 137/N137, 139, 211, 319, 360, C1

For 24-hour London Travel Information, call 020 7222 1234 or visit www.tfl.gov.uk

Note that both the Royal Albert Hall and Cadogan Hall lie outside the Congestion Charging Zone. For car parking at the Royal Albert Hall, see page 137.

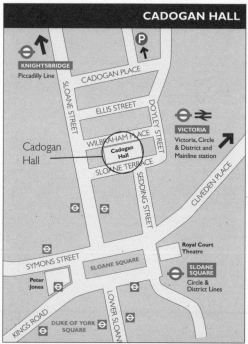

CADOGAN HALL

KNIGHTSBRIDGE
Piccadilly Line

CADOGAN PLACE

SLOANE STREET

ELLIS STREET

DOYLEY STREET

WILBRAHAM PLACE

Cadogan Hall

SLOANE TERRACE

SEDDING STREET

VICTORIA
Victoria, Circle & District and Mainline station

CLIVEDEN PLACE

Royal Court Theatre

SYMONS STREET

SLOANE SQUARE

SLOANE SQUARE
Circle & District Lines

Peter Jones

LOWER SLOANE

KINGS ROAD

DUKE OF YORK SQUARE

Every Prom live on BBC Radio 3 and bbc.co.uk/proms • Advance Booking from 16 May • General Booking from 13 June: 020 7589 8212

135

HOW TO PROM AT THE ROYAL ALBERT HALL

What is Promming?

The popular tradition of Promming is central to the unique and informal atmosphere of the BBC Proms at the Royal Albert Hall.

Up to 1,400 standing places are available at each Proms concert. The traditionally low prices allow you to enjoy world-class concerts for just £4.00 each (or even less with a Season Ticket or Weekend Promming Pass). There are two standing areas: the Arena, located directly in front of the stage, and the Gallery, running round the top of the Hall. All spaces are unreserved.

Day Prommers

Over 500 Arena and Gallery tickets (priced £4.00) go on sale on the day 30 minutes before doors open (one hour before on days when there are Pre-Prom Talks). These tickets cannot be booked in advance, so even if all seats have been sold, you always have a good chance of getting in (though early queuing is obviously advisable for the more popular concerts). You must buy your ticket in person.

Wheelchair-users who wish to Prom (Gallery only) should queue in the same way but will be redirected to Door 8 once their ticket is purchased. (For further information for disabled concert-goers, see page 138.)

Day tickets are available (for cash only) at Door 11 (Arena) and Door 10 (Gallery), not at the Box Office. If in doubt about where to go, Royal Albert Hall stewards will point you in the right direction.

Season Tickets

Frequent Prommers can save money by purchasing Arena or Gallery Season Tickets covering either the whole Proms season (including the Last Night) or only the first or second half (ie Proms 1–37 or Proms 38–73, excluding the Last Night).

Season Ticket-holders benefit from:
- guaranteed entrance (until 10 minutes before each concert)
- great savings – prices can work out at less than £2.00 per concert
- guaranteed entrance to the Last Night for Whole Season Ticket-holders and special access to a reserved allocation of Last Night tickets for Half Season Ticket-holders. See page 139.

Please note that Season Ticket-holders arriving at the Hall later than 10 minutes before a concert are not guaranteed entry and may be asked, in certain circumstances, to join the day queue.

Please note that Season Tickets are non-transferable and two passport-sized photographs must be provided before tickets can be issued.

For further details and prices of Season Tickets, see page 141.

For further details and prices of Weekend Promming Passes, see page 134.

Proms Chamber Music at Cadogan Hall

For details of Gallery Day Tickets and PCM Series Passes, see page 115.

Where to Queue

- Arena Day Queue
  Enter by Door 11

- Gallery Day Queue
  Enter by Door 10

- Arena Season Queue
  Enter by Door 1

- Gallery Season Queue
  Enter by Door 2

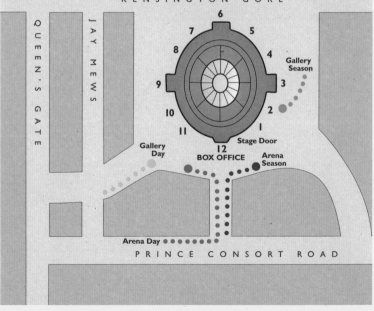

KENSINGTON GORE

QUEEN'S GATE

JAY MEWS

6
7
5
8
4
Gallery Season
9
3
10
2
11
1
12
Stage Door
Gallery Day
BOX OFFICE
Arena Season
Arena Day
PRINCE CONSORT ROAD

Every Prom live on BBC Radio 3 and bbc.co.uk/proms • Advance Booking from 16 May • General Booking from 13 June: 020 7589 8212

136

AT THE ROYAL ALBERT HALL

Restaurants
The Royal Albert Hall offers a choice of three restaurants.

The Elgar Restaurant offers a fine dining experience with full table service. Enter via Door 8 to Circle level.

The Victoria Restaurant offers an Italian menu of light starters, pizza and pasta. Enter via Door 1 to Circle level.

The Café Consort offers a full menu, including salads, sandwiches and light meals. It is now also open in the daytime, offering coffee and a selection of light meals, as well as for meals after the concert on selected dates (call 020 7589 8212 for details). Enter via Door 12.

The Victoria and Elgar Restaurants open two hours before the performance start-time; the Café Consort opens two and half hours before the start-time.

All restaurants can be booked in advance. Call 020 7589 8212 to make a reservation or visit www.royalalberthall.com for more information.

Bars
The Champagne and North Circle bars, offering a range of sandwiches and snacks, open two hours before the start of the performance. All other bars open 45 minutes before the start of the performance.

Catering in your box
Offering sandwiches, a two-course supper with a full range of beverages or simply interval drinks, hospitality can be pre-ordered by telephoning 020 7589 5666. Please allow two working days' notice.

Please note that you are not permitted to consume your own food and drink inside the Hall.
For safety reasons, glasses and bottles are not allowed in the auditorium except as part of box hospitality ordered through the Hall's caterers.

Car Parking A limited number of parking spaces are available from 6.00pm in the Imperial College Car Park (Prince Consort or Exhibition Road entrances). These can be booked in advance (priced £7.50) by ticking the appropriate column on the Advance Booking Form (facing page 142) or by telephoning the Box Office (open 9.00am–9.00pm daily, from 13 June) on 020 7589 8212. Please note that, if attending both early-evening and late-night concerts, only one parking fee is payable.

Smoking is permitted in the following areas only: North Circle Bar; Bars and Foyers at Door 3 (including the ground-floor foyer but excluding the East Porch bar); West Arena Bar. Smoking is banned in all other areas.

Doors open 45 minutes before each concert (earlier for restaurant and bar access).

Latecomers will not be admitted into the auditorium unless or until there is a suitable break in the music. There is a video monitor with digital audio relay in the foyer at Door 6.

Bags and coats may be left in the cloakrooms at Door 9 (ground level) and at basement level beneath Door 6. Folding chairs and hand-luggage larger than a briefcase are not allowed in the auditorium.

Security In the interests of audience safety, bags may be searched upon entry.

Children under 5 Out of consideration for both audience and artists, children under the age of 5 are not allowed in the auditorium.

Dress Code There is no dress code at the Proms.

Mobile phones and watch alarms should be turned off.

The use of cameras, video cameras and recording equipment is strictly forbidden.

Royal Albert Hall Tour & Shop
Tours run daily from Friday to Tuesday and last around 45 minutes. Telephone 020 7838 3105 for further information and to check times. Ticket prices range from £3.50 to £6.00 with a number of concessions available.

The Royal Albert Hall Shop, offering a selection of Proms and Royal Albert Hall gifts and souvenirs, is located in the South Porch at Door 12. The Shop is open daily from 10.00am to 8.00pm. Proms merchandise can also be purchased at Door 6 foyer during performance times.

Every Prom live on BBC Radio 3 and bbc.co.uk/proms • Advance Booking from 16 May • General Booking from 13 June: 020 7589 8212

137

INFORMATION FOR DISABLED CONCERT-GOERS

Access at the Proms

Call the Access Information Line on 020 7838 3110 for advice on facilities for disabled concert-goers (including car parking) at all Proms venues; if you have any special requirements; or to request a Royal Albert Hall Access leaflet. Dedicated staff will be available daily from 9.00am to 9.00pm. The Access leaflet is also available from the Hall's website – www.royalalberthall.com.

 Wheelchair access is available at all Proms venues, but advance booking is advised.

Royal Albert Hall

The Royal Albert Hall has up to 14 spaces bookable in the Stalls for wheelchair-users and their companions (entrance via Door 8). End-of-aisle places are priced as Centre Stalls seats; front-row platform spaces either side of the stage are priced as Side Stalls seats; rear platform places are priced as Front Circle seats. There are up to six spaces in the Front Circle, priced as such. When filling in the Booking Form, tick your preferred price range (ie Centre Stalls, Side Stalls or Front Circle) and enter the number of places required under the 'Wheelchair space' column.

Four wheelchair spaces are available in the Gallery for Promming. These cannot be pre-booked. (See page 136 for 'How to Prom at the Royal Albert Hall'.)

Passenger lifts at the Royal Albert Hall are located on the ground-floor corridor at Doors 1 and 8. Use of lifts is discouraged during performances.

Cadogan Hall

Cadogan Hall has a range of services to assist disabled customers, including a provision for wheelchair-users in the Stalls. There are three wheelchair spaces available for advance booking and one space reserved for sale from 10.00am on the day of the concert. For information, call 020 7730 4500.

Discounts

Disabled concert-goers (and one companion) receive a 50% discount on all ticket prices (except Arena and Gallery areas) for concerts at the Royal Albert Hall and for Proms Chamber Music concerts at Cadogan Hall. To claim this discount, tick the box on Part 3 of the Booking Form, or call the Access Information Line on 020 7838 3110 if booking by phone (from Monday 13 June). Note that discounts for disabled concert-goers cannot be combined with other ticket offers.

Tickets can also be purchased in person from Monday 13 June at the Royal Albert Hall. The Box Office is situated at Door 12 and has ramped access, an induction loop and drop-down counters.

 The Royal Albert Hall has an infra-red system with a number of personal receivers for use with and without hearing aids. To make use of the service, collect a free receiver from the Door 6 Information Desk.

 If you have a guide dog, the best place to sit in the Royal Albert Hall is in a Loggia or Second Tier Box, where your dog may stay with you. If you are sitting elsewhere, stewards will be happy to look after your dog while you enjoy the concert. Please call the Access Information Line on 020 7838 3110 to organise in advance of your visit.

Proms Guide: non-print versions

Audio cassette, CD, braille and computer disk versions of this Guide are available in two parts, 'Articles' and 'Concert Listings/Booking Information', priced £2.50 each or £5 for both.

For more information and to order, contact RNIB Customer Services: 0845 7023 153.

Radio 3 commentary

Visually-impaired patrons are welcome to use the free infra-red hearing facility (see above) to listen in to the broadcast commentary on Radio 3.

Programme-reading service

Ask at the Door 6 Information Desk if you would like a steward to read your concert programme out to you.

Large-print programmes & texts

Large-print concert programmes can be made available on the night (at the same price as the standard programme) if ordered not less than five working days in advance. Complimentary large-print texts and opera librettos (where applicable) can also be made available on the night if ordered in advance. To order any large-print programmes or texts, please telephone 020 7765 3260. They will be left for collection at the Door 6 Information Desk 45 minutes before the start of the concert.

Every Prom live on BBC Radio 3 and bbc.co.uk/proms • Advance Booking from 16 May • General Booking from 13 June: 020 7589 8212

138

THE LAST NIGHT

Owing to the huge demand for Last Night tickets, special booking arrangements apply. Your best chance of purchasing tickets for the Last Night of the Proms is through the Advance Booking system

Advance Booking for the Last Night

The Six Concert Rule

In order to apply for any tickets for the Last Night during the Advance Booking period (ie before General Booking opens on Monday 13 June), you must book for at least six other concerts in the 2005 season.

Book one ticket in the same seating area for at least six other concerts in the 2005 season and you can apply at the same time for a single ticket in the same seating area for the Last Night. For example, book a ticket in the Choir for six concerts, and you can apply for one ticket in the Choir for the Last Night.

Book two or more tickets in the same seating area for at least six other concerts in the 2005 season and you can apply at the same time for a maximum of two tickets in the same seating area for the Last Night (ie whether you book two or 22 Stalls tickets for six concerts, you can still apply for only two Stalls tickets for the Last Night).

Note that, if you book tickets for at least six other concerts but in different seating areas, you will be allocated Last Night seats in the area of the majority of your bookings (unless you specify that lower-priced tickets are desired).

We regret that, if the Last Night is sold out by the time your application is processed, no refunds for other tickets purchased will be payable.

General Bookin[g] the Last Night

Once General Bookin[g] Monday 13 June), the[...] no longer applies. Last [...] usually sold out by th[...] occasionally become [...] so it's always worth c[...] Box Office.

Please note that, for al[...] only one application (f[...] tickets) can be made [...]

Promming at th[e...]

Day Prommers an[d] Promming Pass hol[ders...]

attended six or more [...] either the Arena or t[...] one ticket each for th[...] £4.00) on presentatio[n...] tickets at the Box Off[ice...] Thursday 21 July (sub[...]

Season Ticket-hol[ders]

Tickets include admiss[...] Night. A limited alloca[...] places is also reserve[d...] Ticket-holders. Holde[...] Season Tickets can bu[...] (priced £4.00) at the [...] Thursday 21 July (sub[...] Holders of Second H[...] can buy tickets in the [...] Wednesday 17 Augus[...] availability).

Queuing Whole Se[...] and other Prommers [...]

LAST NIGHT BALLOT FORM

Title

Initial

Surname

Address

Postcode

Country

Daytime tel.

Please tick the appropriate boxes

☐ I wish to apply for one ticket (£73.00)

☐ I wish to apply for two tickets (£146.00)

☐ I enclose a cheque made payable to 'Royal Albert Hall' and an SAE. (Cheques will be returned to unsuccessful applicants within two weeks of the ballot.)

☐ Please debit my Visa/Amex/Mastercard/ Switch*

Expiry date ☐☐ / ☐☐   Issue no.* ☐☐

Security code (CVV no.) ☐☐☐
last 3 digits on back of card

Signature

CHOOSE YOUR SEATING AREA

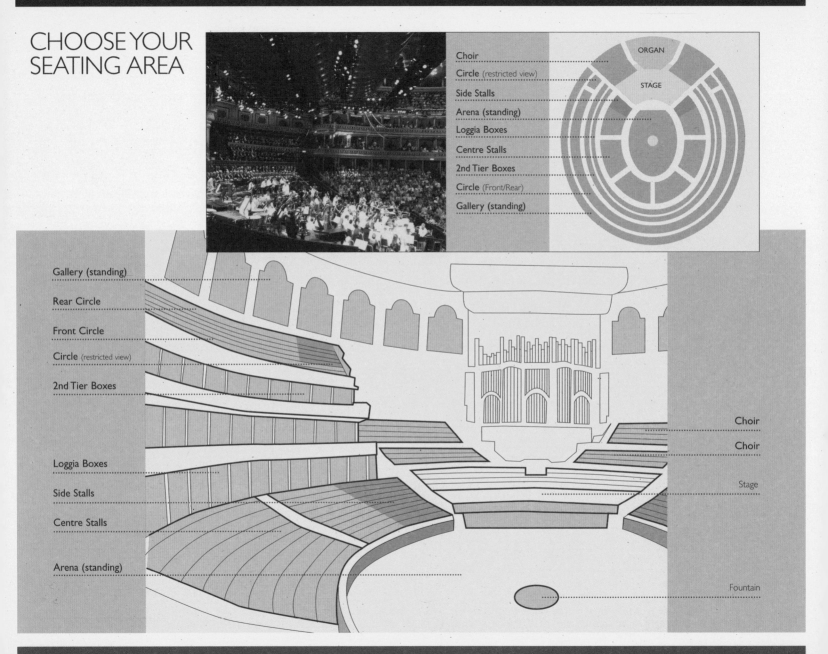

Choir
Circle (restricted view)
Side Stalls
Arena (standing)
Loggia Boxes
Centre Stalls
2nd Tier Boxes
Circle (Front/Rear)
Gallery (standing)

ORGAN
STAGE

Gallery (standing)
Rear Circle
Front Circle
Circle (restricted view)
2nd Tier Boxes
Loggia Boxes
Side Stalls
Centre Stalls
Arena (standing)

Choir
Choir
Stage
Fountain

Every Prom live on BBC Radio 3 and bbc.co.uk/proms • Advance Booking from 16 May • General Booking from 13 June: 020 7589 8212

PRICE BANDS FOR PROMS IN THE ROYAL ALBERT HALL

Seats

Each concert falls into one of seven different price bands, colour-coded for easy reference

	A	B	C	D	E	F	G
Centre Stalls	£23.00	£30.00	£38.00	£12.50	£15.00	£73.00	
Side Stalls	£21.50	£27.00	£35.00	£12.50	£15.00	£70.00	
Loggia Boxes (8 seats)	£25.00	£32.50	£40.00	£12.50	£15.00	£75.00	ALL SEATS £10.00 (UNDER-16s £5.00)
2nd Tier Boxes (5 seats)	£17.50	£22.50	£32.00	£12.50	£15.00	£70.00	
Choir	£15.00	£18.00	£24.00	N/A	N/A	£52.50	
Front Circle	£13.00	£16.00	£20.00	£9.00	£12.50	£52.50	
Rear Circle	£10.00	£11.00	£14.50	£9.00	£12.50	£40.00	
Circle (restricted view)	£6.00	£7.00	£10.00	N/A	N/A	£20.00	

Promming

Standing places are available in the Arena and Gallery on the day for £4.00 (see page 136)

Season Tickets	Dates	Arena	Gallery
Whole Season (Proms 1–74)	15 July – 10 September	**£160.00**	**£135.00**
Half Season tickets			
First Half (Proms 1–37)	15 July – 11 August	**£90.00**	**£75.00**
Second Half (Proms 38–73)	12 August – 9 September	**£90.00**	**£75.00**

BBC Proms in the Park, London, Saturday 10 September

All tickets £20.00   (for further details of this and other Proms in the Park venues, see page 111-113)

BBC Family Prom in the Park, London, Sunday 11 September

Adults £14.00   Children (3–16 yrs) £9.00   Under-3s free

Please note that booking fees apply to all postal, fax, telephone and online bookings (for details, see Booking Form).

Unwanted tickets may be exchanged for tickets to other Proms concerts (subject to availability). A fee of £1.00 per ticket will be charged for this service. Telephone the Royal Albert Hall Box Office (020 7589 8212) for further details.

Express Bookings

All booking forms that include a request for an A band concert qualify for express booking. To increase your chances of getting the tickets you want for popular concerts in price bands B and C, you should book for an A band concert too. If you are booking for a Blue Peter Prom only (price band G), your booking will also qualify for express booking. Tick the box at the end of the Booking Form if your application qualifies.

Disabled Concert-goers

See page 138 for details of special discounts, access and facilities.

Privately-owned Seats

A high proportion of boxes, as well as 650 Stalls seats, are privately owned. Unless returned by owners, these seats are not available for sale.

Season Tickets

Season Tickets and PCM Series Passes can be booked by post, fax or online from 16 May and by phone or in person at the Box Office from 13 June. For postal and fax bookings, complete the special section of the Booking Form (facing page 142). Two passport-sized photographs must be provided for each ticket or pass before it can be issued.

Proms Chamber Music

For booking details, see pages 114–117.

Free Events

For details of tickets to free Proms Extras events, see pages 125–127.

Every Prom live on BBC Radio 3 and bbc.co.uk/proms • Advance Booking from 16 May • General Booking from 13 June: 020 7589 8212

141

HOW TO FILL IN THE ADVANCE BOOKING FORM

- **Choose the concerts** you want to go to and where you want to sit.

- **Enter the number of tickets** you require for each concert under your chosen seating area (adult tickets on the white squares, under-16s on the blue).

- **Add up the value of tickets** requested and enter the amount in the 'Sub-total' column.

- **If claiming any special offers** (see page 134) or disabled concert-goers' discounts (see page 138), enter the total value of discounts claimed for each concert in the red 'Discount' column. Then subtract the value of the discount from the 'Sub-total' and enter the 'Total' at the end of the row (adding in any Car Parking fee, if applicable).

- **If the tickets you request are not available**, you can opt to receive either lower-priced or higher-priced alternatives by ticking the appropriate box at the end of the Booking Form.

Booking Queries

If you have any queries about how to fill in the Booking Form, call the Box Office on 020 7589 8212 (open 9.00am–9.00pm daily).

Fax Booking

If booking by fax, clearly enter your name at the top of all three pages and tick the box at the end of Part 3. Please do not duplicate your fax booking by post or online. Note that fax booking lines are open 24 hours a day.

Online Ticket Request System

For details of how to book online, visit the BBC Proms website at bbc.co.uk/proms

ADVANCE BOOKING FORM PART 1

Full name of sender **Surname** **First Name**

Prom No. / Date	Time (Same Day Saver See page 134)	Price Code	Centre Stalls	Side Stalls	Loggia Boxes (8 seats)	2nd Tier Boxes (5 seats)	Choir	Front Circle	Rear Circle	Circle (restricted view)	Wheelchair space (See page 138)	Sub-total (£)	Discount (£)	Car Parking (See page 137)	Total (£)	Office Use
1 Friday 15 July	7.00	B										..	..		..	
2 Saturday 16 July	7.30	B										..	..		..	
3 Sunday 17 July	6.30	A										..	..		..	
4 Monday 18 July	5.00	C										..	..	X	..	
5 Tuesday 19 July	7.00	A										..	..		..	
6 Wednesday 20 July	7.00	A										..	..		..	
7 Wednesday 20 July	10.15	E					X			X		..	..		..	
8 Thursday 21 July	7.30	A										..	..		..	
9 Friday 22 July	7.30	A										..	..		..	
10 Saturday 23 July	11.00	G										..	..	X	..	
11 Saturday 23 July	7.30	A										..	..	X	..	
12 Sunday 24 July	3.30	G										..	..		..	
13 Sunday 24 July	7.30	A										..	..		..	
14 Monday 25 July	7.00	A										..	..		..	
15 Tuesday 26 July	7.30	A										..	..		..	
16 Wednesday 27 July	7.00	A										..	..		..	
17 Wednesday 27 July	10.00	D					X			X		..	..		..	
18 Thursday 28 July	7.30	A										..	..		..	
19 Friday 29 July	7.30	A										..	..		..	

= Number of adults = Number of under-16s

Discount (£) For special offers and discounts, see pages 134 & 138. Enter value of discount here

BBC Proms, Box Office, Royal Albert Hall, London SW7 2AP

Fax number:

020 7581 9311

If you fax this booking form, please do not duplicate your order by post or online

PART I

ADVANCE BOOKING FORM PART 2

Full name of sender   Surname   First Name

Date / Prom No.	Time (Same Day Saver — See page 134)	Price Code	Centre Stalls	Side Stalls	Loggia Boxes (8 seats)	2nd Tier Boxes (5 seats)	Choir	Front Circle	Rear Circle	Circle (restricted view)	Wheelchair space (See page 138)	Sub-total (£)	Discount (£)	Car Parking (See page 137)	Total (£)	Office Use
56 Friday 26 August	7.30	A										..	..		..	..
57 Saturday 27 August	7.30	C										..	..		..	..
58 Sunday 28 August	6.30	B										..	..		..	..
59 Monday 29 August	7.30	B										..	..		..	..
60 Tuesday 30 August	7.00	C										..	..		..	..
61 Tuesday 30 August	10.00	D					✕			✕		..	..		..	..
62 Wednesday 31 August	7.30	C										..	..		..	..
63 Thursday 1 September	7.00	C										..	..		..	..
64 Thursday 1 September	10.00	E					✕			✕		..	..		..	..
65 Friday 2 September	7.30	C										..	..		..	..
66 Saturday 3 September	7.00	A										..	..		..	..
67 Sunday 4 September	6.30	A										..	..		..	..
68 Monday 5 September	7.00	A										..	..		..	..
69 Tuesday 6 September	7.00	A										..	..		..	..
70 Tuesday 6 September	10.00	D					✕			✕		..	..		..	..
71 Wednesday 7 September	7.30	C										..	..		..	..
72 Thursday 8 September	7.30	C										..	..	.	..	..
73 Friday 9 September	7.30	B										..	..		..	..

☐ = Number of adults   ☐ = Number of under-16s

Total carried over

Discount (£) — For special offers and discounts, see pages 134 & 138. Enter value of discount here

TEAR ALONG THE PERFORATED LINE

**BBC Proms, Box Office,
Royal Albert Hall, London SW7 2AP**

Fax number:
020 7581 9311

If you fax this booking form, please do not duplicate your order by post or online

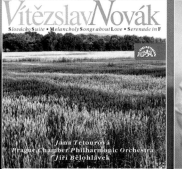

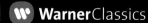

PROMS
MERCHANDISING

The new Proms range:

T-shirts, bags, mugs, pens and more.
Available from the Royal Albert Hall Shop (Door 12)
and at the Door 6 foyer.

The perfect gift for Friends & Family.

BBC PROMS
15 JULY – 10 SEPTEMBER 2005

CHAMBER ORCHESTRA OF EUROPE 2006

SILVER JUBILEE SEASON AT THE QUEEN ELIZABETH HALL

Sat 7 Jan 2006, 7.30pm

Chabrier Suite pastorale
Mahler Lieder eines fahrenden gesellen
Beethoven Symphony No.6 'Pastoral'

Philippe Jordan conductor
Anne Sofie von Otter mezzo-soprano

Tue 16 May 2006, 7.30pm
Programme includes:
Berlioz Symphonie fantastique

Douglas Boyd conductor
special guests to be announced

Thu 28 Sep 2006, 7.30pm

Mozart Symphony No.29 in A
Mozart Piano Concerto No.19 in F, K.459
Mozart Piano Concerto No.9 in E flat, K.271

Pierre-Laurent Aimard conductor/piano

Tickets £35 £27 £20 £12 £8

Premium Seats £50
Concessions 50% off (limited availability)
Series Offer 15% off when you book for all 3 concerts

Box Office 0870 3800 400
www.rfh.org.uk/coe

Index of Artists

Bold italic figures refer to Prom numbers
(PCM indicates Proms Chamber Music concerts: see pages 114–117).
* First appearance at a BBC Henry Wood Promenade Concert

Index of Works

Bold italic figures refer to Prom numbers (PCM indicates Proms Chamber Music concerts: see pages 114–117).
* First performance at a BBC Henry Wood Promenade Concert